THE
UNIVERSE OF LIGHT

BY

SIR WILLIAM BRAGG

CXTSA

DOVER PUBLICATIONS, INC.
NEW YORK

Published in Canada by General Publishing Company, Ltd., 30 Lesmill Road, Don Mills, Toronto, Ontario.

This Dover edition, first published in 1959, is an unabridged and unaltered republication of the work originally published by G. Bell and Sons, Ltd. in 1933. This edition is published by special arrangement with G. Bell and Sons, Ltd.

International Standard Book Number: 0-486-20538-X
Library of Congress Catalog Card Number: 59-65237

Manufactured in the United States of America
Dover Publications, Inc.
180 Varick Street
New York, N. Y. 10014

PREFACE

THE recent advances of physical science have aroused wide-spread attention, all the more because the fascinating problems to which they lead have been described by writers of singular ability. I have thought that I might add something to the appreciation of this new knowledge by writing a short account of the earlier researches from which the present developments have arisen. The experiments and reasonings of Newton and Huygens, Young and Fresnel, Crookes and Thomson and many other workers past and present built the roads leading to the positions which now we occupy. We do not grasp in full the significance of these positions unless we know something of the country over which the previous travelling has been done.

I have taken as the thread of my story that old rivalry between two theories of light which has been one of the most powerful contributors to the development of science. The corpuscle and the wave, associated always with the names, respectively, of Newton and Huygens have each in turn seemed to be finally victorious. The struggle is ending in a manner as unexpected as it is illuminating. There is to be a reconcilement of hypotheses which we had thought to be mutually exclusive; and the fact warns us of the danger of allowing our mental imaginings to become fixed beliefs. We still find it difficult to understand how these two theories can both be true; yet we are forced to do so by the mass of good evidence which can be brought forward in support of each of them. We conclude that what at one time may be beyond our understanding may later become clear, not only through the acquisition of fresh knowledge, but also by the training of our minds to new ways of thought.

It is sure that the researches of the future based upon a combination of the two old theories will be as fruitful as in the past when they have lived and thrived on their rivalry.

Light properly so called is only a narrowly defined part of a far greater phenomenon, that of radiation in general. But the laws of optics are applicable over the greater range, and the work of the pioneers had a wider meaning than they knew. The lengths of light waves fall between close limits: but the rules of the wave motion apply to the infinitesimal waves of the Röntgen rays on the one hand and to the long radio waves on the other. The investigations that are founded on the use of light have also a tremendous range. They deal with the vast spaces of astronomy, and with the minute structures whose ordered intricacies are equally beyond the reach of our eyes; and they find that both fields of research are crowded with matters of the deepest interest.

Moreover, radiations which are obviously corpuscular such as the showers of electrons and protons and atoms which are now produced so easily in our laboratories are found to-day to obey in some measure the laws of light. The wave and the corpuscle are different aspects rather than different entities. In a word light dominates physical science and indeed all sciences. The growth of physics has depended upon the study of its various forms and properties, and the new developments which fascinate us are still its consequences. It is one long story; and this book is meant to give a short account of some of its earlier incidents so that the later may be the more easily appreciated.

The title of the book is also that of a course of lectures which I gave at Christmas time in 1931 at the Royal Institution. These courses have been given annually for more than a century to audiences consisting largely of young people. Faraday himself gave no less than nineteen of them. The simplicity and clearness of his exposition and the aptness of his experimental illustrations were especially 'adapted to a juvenile auditory' to use the quaint phrase still appearing in the annual advertisement. His successors have tried to do as he did. The Christmas Lectures of 1931 were therefore fully illustrated by experiment, some old, some a little new. I have made use of them in this book, but I have of course carried their description and the arguments based upon them much further than was proper or possible during the lectures.

I have occasion to be grateful to many friends who have helped me to illustrate the book. Mr. Thorne Baker has taken most of the coloured photographs without which a book on light becomes very ineffective. The drawings in 'pen and wash' are due to my daughter, Mrs. Alban Caroe. Professor C. T. R. Wilson has allowed me to reproduce many of his expansion photographs. The infra-red photograph of a landscape was given to me by Messrs. Ilford Ltd. Professor A. Fowler and Dr. W. M. Smart have kindly supplied me with photographs of spectra, and Professor Andrade with illustrations of diffraction. The diagram on p. 131 was suggested by Dr. W. T. Astbury. Most of the photographs of experimental arrangements have been made in the Royal Institution by Mr. W. J. Green and his assistant Mr. K. Bridger. I have tried to make further acknowledgements in their appropriate places.

W. H. BRAGG.

CONTENTS

CONTENTS

LIST OF PLATES

THE UNIVERSE OF LIGHT

CHAPTER I

THE NATURE OF LIGHT

LIGHT brings us the news of the Universe. Coming to us from the sun and the stars it tells us of their existence, their positions, their movements, their constitutions and many other matters of interest. Coming to us from objects that surround us more nearly it enables us to see our way about the world: we enjoy the forms and colours that it reveals to us, we use it in the exchange of information and thought. If the meaning of the word is extended, as may be done with every right and reason, to cover the wide range of radiations which are akin to it and yet are not visible to the eye, then light is also the great conveyer of energy from place to place in the world and in the universe, principally by the transfer of what we call 'heat.' The modern transmission of radio is also covered by the term, and so are the Röntgen rays, rays from radio-active substances, and, possibly, the cosmic rays which have lately excited so much interest. These greatly differing phenomena are all manifestations of one principle, the magnificent inclusiveness of which has grown clearer continuously as we have studied the nature of light.

We may go even further. In the last few years, it has become clear that the individual electron, the minute element of electricity, has properties akin to those radiations of which light is typical and familiar. Even the atoms themselves seem to fall, in certain aspects, within the same great category.

Light. therefore, using the full meaning of the word, transmits energy which is the mainstay of life, and gives to living beings the power of observation: and it is akin to the matter of which all things animate and inanimate are made. The universe is its sphere of action. We do it no more than justice when we speak of the Universe of Light.

We must first consider light in the narrower sense, as that which our eyes perceive. A ray of sunlight leaves its source and comes to us in due time. On its way it has gone through various experiences. It has crossed the heated gas layers on the surface of the sun, and the atmosphere that surrounds the earth. It has been reflected perhaps many times, and finally it comes to us from the object at which we are looking. This last reflection is to us the most important part of its journey, because it helps us to make out where the object is, and what is its character. Our eyes can gather a little more than that: the training that experience has given them enables us to recognise the source from which the light has come. We do not mistake it for some form of artificial light. When we use instruments which analyse the sun's light we can do far more. We can infer the nature of the experiences that the light has met with on its journey: we can discover the composition and state of the atmospheres that it has gone through, and something of the bodies which have reflected it.

When one watches an ocean liner at the end of a voyage moving slowly into her place in the docks, her appearance tells at once her port of origin and her voyage, and if one goes on board, the objects that the passengers have in their hands, or that are lying about, speak of the ports where the ship has called. The story of the voyage is written in these details.

Just so a ray of light on arrival at the eye brings with it the story of its experiences, some easily read, some with difficulty. The piece of news of which the eyes make the most, is that which tells of the last scattering before the ray came to the end of its journey; it is that which enables the eyes to 'see' the object where that scattering took place.

The Wave Theory of Light

So we come naturally to the question as to the nature of this messenger and as to the means by which it travels from place to place. In these days it is much easier to understand the recognised explanation than it was even a few years ago. Transmission by radio, broadcasting as we generally call it in this country, has made us familiar with the idea of a disturbance or condition which travels in waves from a central station and is interpreted by 'receiving sets' near and far. The sun sends out waves just as the central station does: our eyes receive and interpret the wave motions that strike them, just as our wireless sets receive and interpret the waves from the 'studio.' There is no difference whatever in kind between the two sets of waves: there is a difference only in their dimensions. They travel at exactly the same rate; whatever medium carries the one, carries the other also. The one difference lies in the fact that the waves of light follow one another at far smaller intervals

3

than the radio waves. This difference has of course its consequences, so that in several ways light and radio transmission do not behave alike. The point is that fundamentally they are of the same nature.

It is both interesting and helpful that this similarity exists. The wave theory of light has always been difficult to comprehend because the central idea has been so strange. But now the newspapers tell us every day the lengths of the waves that are sent out from the various stations, and so the conception of waves has become quite familiar. Of course that does not mean that now we all know what sort of medium carries these waves, and how this medium is distributed in the world and in space. Nor have we necessarily learnt what it is that moves to and fro, or up and down, or indeed, what sort of a motion there is to correspond to the familiar wave movement of the water on the surface of the sea. In fact all that most people know is that there are waves in the radio which can be measured with some accuracy, and that the receiving set can be adjusted to the wave-length which any particular station sends out. But this is quite useful when we try to grasp what is meant by the wave theory of light. We see that the radio engineer makes daily use of the wave conception, and regulates his business by it. The idea seems to lose its haziness and become practical even though, when we look more closely into the matter, we find we do not really know much more than we did before. We gain also because the considerable differences in behaviour of the two kinds of waves are instructive. We can appeal to them on many occasions, as we shall see.

4

The wave-length of the radio from the Daventry station is 1,554.4 metres, or 155,440 centimetres. The wave-length of red light is rather less than the ten thousandth part of one centimetre. We wish to make experiments which will illustrate visibly some of the properties of waves. Clearly radio waves are far too long, and light waves far too short for the purpose. We must use some wave motion of more convenient dimensions, and we find it in the movement of water ripples. Let us proceed to water ripples therefore; we are quite justified in using them to help us because they will tell us the chief characteristics of wave motion as well as any other example; long or short, all wave motions behave alike in the main.

Experiments with Ripples

We use a shallow tank with a glass bottom as shown in Fig. 1. It contains water to a depth of about a quarter of an inch. The ripples that run over the water when it is disturbed are not easy to follow when viewed directly, but we can watch them very easily if we use a naked light and project their shadows by means of a mirror upon the screen.

We give the tank a jolt so as to start ripples parallel to one side. They run across the tank both ways and the two sets cross in the middle. They pass through each other and each comes at last to the opposite side from which it started. There it recoils and comes back the way it went. These two observations which we make so easily illustrate two of the most fundamental characteristics of wave motions.

The first shows us how two sets of waves pass through one another without alteration of either set. This is a familiar fact to all of us even though we may not have realised it. There would be queer happenings if it were not so. Suppose that someone is looking at a candle; it is sending its light rays to his eyes. Suppose that a second person is looking at another candle and that the two lines of sight cross each other. Each sees the candle he

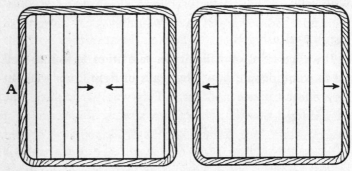

Fig. 1. A jolt given to the ripple tank starts waves which cross it. The two sets which originate at two sides are approaching each other in the one picture and have passed through each other in the second.

looks at as well as if the other were not there; if this were not so the fact would be only too obvious. Think how surprising it would be if all the rays of light scattered from the various objects in a room damaged each other in some way at every one of their multitudinous crossings. Nothing would be recognised in the jumble; the whole room would be a blur and no more. So also the rays from the various broadcasting services do not damage each other where they cross. The effect known technically as 'interference' is of a different and peculiar nature which we shall examine later. When an observer,

6

say in London, listens to the radio station at Cardiff, and someone in Southampton listens to Daventry, neither finds an ill effect from the fact that the two sets of waves cross each other, as they do somewhere about Oxford. There is a complicated movement during the crossing of sets of rays, but once it is over each set of waves passes on its way as if it had never been involved with the other. Trains of waves pass through each other without any mutual effects, and this is obviously of enormous importance in explaining our powers of vision.

It was certainly a difficulty in past times, as it may well be to some people now, that rays of light cross without any effect on one another. This was particularly the case if light was thought of as a stream of corpuscles, a theory which Sir Isaac Newton maintained. It was brought forward as an objection to his hypothesis that two people would not be able to look into each other's eyes, because the corpuscles passing to and fro would hit each other and fall to the ground. It was not a very strong objection because it could be supposed that the corpuscles were so small that encounters rarely took place. It is interesting, however, to see what sort of arguments passed to and fro when philosophers began to consider, with the aid of some experiment, what the nature of light might be.

In Newton's day there were two rival theories: the corpuscular, proposed by Newton himself, and a pulse theory proposed by Huygens, which was the precursor of the wave theories of to-day. Both Newton and Huygens assumed the existence of minute corpuscles.

The former, however, supposed that light consisted of such corpuscles in flight: the latter imagined the corpuscles to be packed together at rest and to fill all space, the propagation of light consisting in the transmission of shocks from corpuscle to corpuscle. To quote from his Treatise on Light:—

'When one takes a number of spheres of equal size, made of some very hard substance, and arranges them in a straight line, so that they touch one another, one finds, on striking with a similar sphere against the first of these spheres, that the motion passes as in an instant to the last of them, which separates itself from the row, without one's being able to perceive that the others have been stirred. And even that one which was used to strike remains motionless with them. Whence one sees that the movement passes with an extreme velocity which is the greater, the greater the hardness of the substance of the spheres.

'But it is still certain that this progression of motion is not instantaneous, but successive, and therefore must take time. For if the movement, or the disposition to movement, if you will have it so, did not pass successively through all these spheres, they would all acquire the movement at the same time, and hence would all advance together; which does not happen.'

Huygens was careful to point out that his pulses did not succeed one another at equal intervals. Thus he disclaimed the regularity which is an essential property of a wave motion: the property of which Young and Fresnel made such successful use at the beginning of the nineteenth century when they laid the foundations of the modern theory of light. We shall consider later Young's development of the principle of interference and Fresnel's of the principle of the transverse wave. Huygens was however able to explain the simpler phenomena of light by means of his pulses, including reflection and the crossing of rays without mutual

Fig. 2. The figure is copied from Huygens's Treatise on Light. The ball A, striking one end of a row of balls, comes to rest, but a ball at the other end moves off.

injury. The latter he explained with the aid of a figure which is here reproduced (Fig. 2). He observes that if the hard spheres A and D are pushed from opposite sides so as to strike the block of spheres at the same time, they rebound as if they had struck a fixed body. The pulses must have passed through the block in opposite direction: so that the motion of A is communicated to D, and vice versa (Fig. 2).

The experiment may be arranged in another way. Balls are arranged on a board as in the figure: they are kept in line by shallow grooves cut in the board. If now A is rolled towards B and D to E, so as to strike simultaneously, A and D stay in contact with B and E respectively while C and F roll away. The two pulses have crossed each other at the centre of the figure without mutual effect (Fig. 3).

After Newton the corpuscular theory lost ground and

the wave theory eventually triumphed, because when modified and extended by Young and Fresnel it was found to be capable of explaining, not only all that was known in the time of Newton and Huygens, but many other properties of light which were discovered later. We shall find as we go on that the wave theory still has its power; we shall indeed make extensive use of it, and shall draw many illustrations from the behaviour of

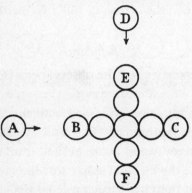

Fig. 3. A variation of the last experiment. The balls A and D strike B and E simultaneously and come to rest. The balls C and F move off.

ripples as we have already begun to do. It is very curious and interesting, however, to find that in recent years still newer facts have come to light which the wave theory is unable to explain clearly; they seem to demand a return to a corpuscular theory like Newton's. Some way has to be found of reconciling observations that seem to be absolutely in opposition to each other; and there has never been so exciting a period in the history of science as this, when the effort to understand seems to strain our mental powers to the uttermost.

We must not pursue this particular enquiry any

further for the moment. We must be content to explore the less intricate characteristics of light, and in doing so are glad of a theory which serves us excellently. We may know all the time that we shall be leaving matters of greater difficulty for some later consideration, but there is no harm in that. We may proceed with the comfortable assurance that in attending to simple matters first, and in trying to express them in terms of a theory which is correct over a certain range at least, we shall not be wasting our time.

Reflection

Now for the second of the observations that we readily make when we watch the ripples move over the water in the tank, viz., the fact of reflection. We have seen that a train of ripples coming broad side on to the edge of the tank is thrown straight back again. If now we set in motion a train which meets the edge obliquely, we see that there is a reflected train which is inclined to the edge of the tank at the same angle as the first train. This corresponds with a well-known property of light; long ago it was asserted that the incident and reflected rays make the same angle with the reflecting surface of a mirror (Fig. 4).

It may be well at this point to consider the relation of the two terms we are using, the 'ray' and the 'train of waves.' We use the term 'ray' to describe for instance the bright shaft of sunlight that streams through a hole in the shutter of a darkened room. It is also to be thought of as a train of waves: but it is impossible to represent the idea correctly in a diagram. It would be necessary to draw parallel lines as in the figure in order to represent the successive waves, and these ought to be drawn so as to indicate that there are about forty thousand waves to the inch, if the representation is to be true. Nevertheless, in considering such a drawing

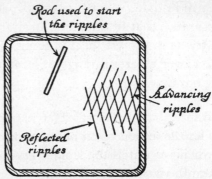

Fig. 4. The figure shows the reflection of ripples at the side of the tank.

one is led to observe an important point. The ends of the waves could not in actual fact be so clearly defined that a line could be ruled through them corresponding to the boundary line of a 'ray.' We should expect them to spread sideways and their edges to become vague. Now this actually happens in the case of the ray of light, and the effect is of great theoretical importance as we shall see later. Practically, the effect is small and may generally be disregarded, so that in most cases we are justified in drawing 'rays' of light as if the light was confined within straight well defined boundaries. The direction of the ray is of course perpendicular to the waves.

Let us make one or two experiments to illustrate the reflection of a ray of light at a plane surface. The lantern

sends out a straight narrow beam (Fig. 5). A single
mirror reflects it, and though we do not stop to make
exact measurements we can easily see that the reflection
law is obeyed at least approximately: and we may accept

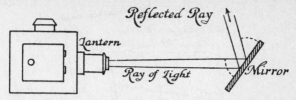

Fig. 5. The incident and reflected rays make the same angle
with the mirror.

an assurance that the most exact experiment finds no
fault in it. As an extension and variation of the experiment we take two mirrors at right angles to each other,
and place them, with their joining line vertical, so that
the horizontal ray falls on one mirror and then after
reflection there, upon the second. After the double
reflection it returns on a line parallel to that on which it

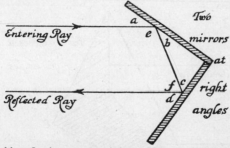

Fig. 6. Double reflection at two mirrors which are at right angles to each
other. The two rays are parallel if the junction of the mirrors is at right
angles to them; because $a + d = b + c = 90°$; $\therefore e + f = 360° - (a+b+c+d)$
$= 180°$.

came: and this is true no matter how the mirrors are
held, as Fig. 6 shows. If, however, the mirrors are
placed so that the joining line is not vertical, the doubly

reflected ray is not parallel to the original (Fig. 7). We obtain a further and particularly interesting illustration of the reflection laws if we construct an arrangement of three mirrors, mutually perpendicular as

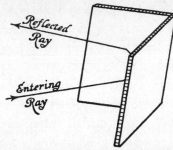

Fig. 7. They are not parallel when the condition of the previous experiment is not satisfied.

in Fig. 8. A ray which strikes and is reflected by all three in turn is sent back in its original direction, no matter how the arrangement is held. This is a device which has been invented and used more than once,

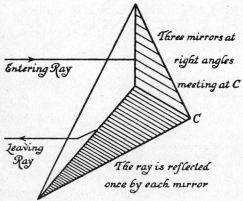

Fig. 8. Reflection from three mirrors at right angles. However the mirrors are held the entering and returning rays are parallel.

14

and the last of its uses is very apt and ingenious. A recent law decided that a bicycle must carry a red reflector which shall send back to the motor driver some of the light from his own headlamp. Reflectors of various kinds were produced at once, but not all could send back the ray from the headlamp with sufficient concentration and direction towards the car. It was necessary to examine them all at the National Physical Laboratory and to select those which satisfied the regulations. Among the best was one which was designed on the three mirror plan of Fig 8. The reflector is a piece of red glass having a flat front, and a back stamped into the form of a number of triangular pyramids, the sides of each pyramid being three planes mutually perpendicular. The light from the car enters the front and parts of it are reflected three times at the three faces of each pyramid, so that a bundle of rays goes back the way it came, that is to say, in the direction of the motor car, which is just what is wanted.

The Scattering of Light

We speak sometimes of the reflection of light, and sometimes of its scattering. It is important to remember that the two terms do not refer to different processes but to different conditions under which one process occurs. If light meets with an obstacle it is turned aside. If the object has a smooth surface the new motion is regular and based on some simple plan determined by the form of the surface. We generally speak of this effect as a reflection. But if the surface is irregular, the light

15

is dispersed in all directions, and we speak of a scattering. When the waves of the sea roll up against a faced embankment, there is a regular and simple reflection: but if the shore is rocky there is a disordered motion and we do not see a train of recoiling waves.

When a ray of light crosses a room, its track is visible because the air of the room holds dust particles of many kinds in suspension, and these turn aside some of the

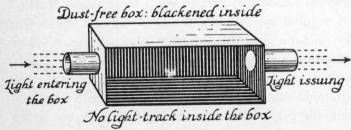

Fig. 9. Light passes through dust-free air without appreciable scattering.

light into our eyes. But if there were no dust the ray would be no longer visible from one side. In order to prove this point, we make use of a box through which the ray can go as in Fig. 9, entering and leaving it by glass windows. The glass front of the box allows the interior to be seen. The walls are blackened on the inside and are coated with glycerine some days before the experiment, so that all dust in the box has accumulated on the sides and remained there, and the air of the box is almost dust free. The ray may then be seen before it enters the box and after it leaves, but is invisible during the crossing. Of course this fits in with our hypothesis. For if the ray of light consists of a train of waves, and if the eye is an organ which acts when light

16

enters it, then if the waves of our ray are no longer turned aside by the dust we no longer see anything of the ray. We might arrange for a ray of light – as strong as we like – to enter a room by one opening and to go out by another, and to leave the room in complete darkness, provided that in the first place, the room was not lit up by any other means, and secondly that its air was free from dust. In fact we might think of this box as approximating to such a room. But if a piece of white

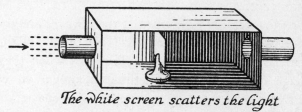

The white screen scatters the light

Fig. 10. A piece of white paper intercepts the light and scatters it, becoming a brilliant secondary source of light.

paper is placed in the path of the rays, the box and the room are illuminated (Fig. 10). It is quite helpful on some occasions to remember how much of a ray can be turned aside in this way. If, for example, one has to change a tyre on the car in a country lane at night and the electric torch has been forgotten and the lamp will not turn round to look in all directions, one can get a fine illumination by holding a piece of white paper in front of a headlight. All this is readily to be understood if the ray consists of a train of waves.

So far then we have found two characteristics in these ripple motions which correspond to properties of light with which we are familiar. They can pass through each other freely and they are reflected at a surface just as light can be. Let us therefore accept as a possibility the hypothesis that light is a wave motion. We ask at once, in what? And we have to admit that we are not aware of any medium in which these waves can move. The air will not serve, because sunlight crosses the space between sun and earth where there is no air at all. But our previous ignorance of the existence of such a medium does not forbid us to suppose that it exists. At any rate we find it convenient for our present purpose to assume its existence.

We may well ask now whether these waves are always carried by the same medium. Are they carried by the air when they go through the air, by glass when they go through glass, and by something unknown on earth when they cross the apparent emptiness of space? The answer to that is that we get a good picture of what happens in all these cases if we suppose that the medium which carries the waves of light fills all space, including places where there are glass or air or anything of that sort: in fact all space whether there are material bodies there or not. We must think of all bodies that we can see or feel as immersed in a universal ocean. We give it a name, the ether. When light crosses a space where there is a material substance the waves are carried by the ether: nevertheless, the substance has its effect, it may slow down the rate at which the waves travel or stop them altogether. We shall go into these matters presently.

But does this strange medium really exist? This is a question which we ask at once. And yet when we come to think what answer we shall give, we begin to doubt whether there is any real meaning to the question, whether in fact it is a proper question at all. We soon get into deep waters if we try to picture to ourselves what is meant by 'really existing.' Fortunately we need not try: and ought not to try: because if we do we shall be straying away from our object which is to gather together our observations on light and find how they are connected with one another. We find that many of them are such as remind us of waves running through a medium, and so adopt this useful way of considering them. It may be that all the effects of light cannot be represented in this way: in fact we find that there are some which cannot be fitted into this scheme. But that does not matter for the moment. When it becomes clear that our first conceptions are insufficient we can modify them or change them altogether. Till then we find them most convenient and helpful.

The Sideways Spreading of a Ray of Light

It may be urged as an objection that if the ray of light which crosses the room consists of a long train of waves rippling through the ether, the ray ought gradually to diffuse itself sideways: that the edges of the ray ought not to be so sharp as we see them to be. The objection is quite natural, and there is, indeed, such a spreading, but it is so very small that it is not in this case observable. That does not happen always: in some circumstances the spreading is a very important matter, causing some of the most striking and even the most beautiful of Nature's sights. That which determines the importance of the spreading of a ray of light is the relation between the length of the wave and the width of the ray. The wavelength of the light that we see is round about the thirty thousandth of an inch, or the ten thousandth of a centimetre, and is very small in comparison with the width of our ray. If the latter were only a small fraction of a centimetre there would be noticeable results from the tendency of the wave motion to spread out sideways, as we shall see later. Suppose that a local storm raises the waves on some part of an ocean and drives them forwards. If the path of the storm is a hundred miles wide the gradual opening out sideways is comparatively small. One may watch the effect on a much smaller scale on the still water of a pond when a puff of wind raises a train of tiny ripples which goes forwards, having an undisturbed surface on either side. Even in these cases the ratio between the wave-length and the width of the ray is far greater than in the case of a ray of light.

Images

Let us now go on to consider another matter which also our ripple tank can illustrate. A finger is dipped in the water and the waves spread out in circles in a way that is quite familiar. They come to an edge of the tank. They are reflected, and we observe that they still preserve the circular form: but the centre of the new set of circles is a point outside the tank. If we imagine a straight line to be drawn between this point and the point where the finger touched the water, the edge of the tank bisects this line at right angles. The reflected ripples seem to be diverging from the new point (Fig. 11).

Just in the same way, when the waves spread out in circles from such a source of light as a candle and fall on the flat and polished surface of a mirror, the waves coming from each point of the candle seem to spread, after reflection, from a corresponding point behind the mirror. If some of these waves enter our eyes we imagine that they actually come from the latter point, and as the light is of the sort that comes from a candle, and as each point of the candle is represented in this way, we imagine that a candle is placed there: for which reason we say that there is an 'image' of the candle in the mirror which is just as far behind the mirror as the candle is in front of it.

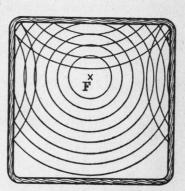

Fig. 11. Reflection of circular ripples at the side of the tank. Originally diverging from F, they appear after reflection to diverge from F'.

Wherever we are when we receive these reflected waves they seem to come from the same point, because their form is spherical – on the ripple tank the motion is plane and the ripples are circular – and they proceed as if from the image as centre. Therefore, when we move our eyes about in front of a flat mirror or look at reflections in the surface of a still sheet of water, the reflected objects seem to keep their places while we move about. Each point of the image is just as far behind the reflecting surface or its continuation as the corresponding point in the original. The accompanying illustrations may help to make this clear (Plate IIA ; Plate III).

Reflection at Curved Surface

When reflections take place in curved mirrors the matter is not so simple, as we know.   If we look into the

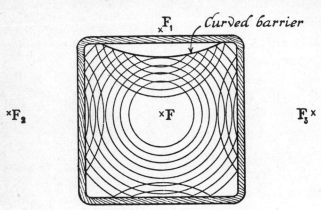

Fig. 12.   Reflection of ripples at a convex surface.   The centre of the reflected ripples F_1, is now much nearer to the surface than the original source F.   The reflected ripples are now only approximately circular: but the difference is only obvious when large arcs are considered.

curved convex mirrors, which are so often used for purposes of decoration, we see the objects of the room collected together there on a diminished scale: also they are somewhat distorted and move slightly as we move our heads.   The ripple tank may be used to illustrate the point.

A curved barrier is placed in the tank to reflect the

PLATE II

A. If a perpendicular line is drawn to join any point in this picture to its image in the water, it is bisected by the water level underneath that point. The artist's intention is to make these levels easy to trace. For example, the water level under the road at the back of the Church is found by continuing a line joining the points where the arch on its nearer face dips into the water on the two sides of the stream. (*p. 22*)

B. A stereoscopic view of a cloister in St. Michel. The two pictures are taken from slightly different points of view. (*p. 28*)

PLATE III

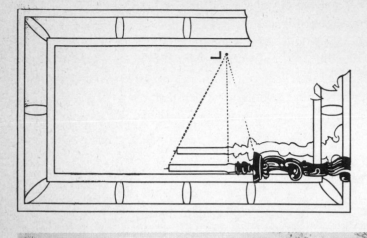

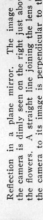

Reflection in a plane mirror. The image of the camera is dimly seen on the right just above the flowers. A straight line joining the lens of the camera to its image is perpendicular to the mirror. So is every other such line, for instance that which joins the top of the candle to its image. All such straight lines meet in the same 'vanishing point' according to the laws of perspective. The drawing illustrates this point. (*p.* 22)

waves: its convexity faces the place of dipping. We now
see that if a set of circular ripples is set going as before,
the reflected set of waves is more sharply curved than the
original. They still seem to come from a point behind
the barrier, but it is not so far behind the barrier as the
point of dipping is in front (Fig. 12). The same effect
must occur in the case of light: it is illustrated in Fig. 13.
From this experiment we may see why, when we look at

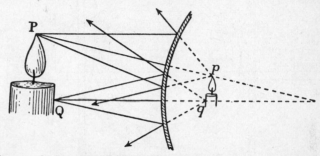

Fig. 13. Optical reflection at a convex mirror. The rays from P and Q
seem after reflection to come from *p* and *q* respectively. Any eye receiving
some of the reflected rays imagines that there is a candle at *p q*, reduced in
size.

an image in a convex mirror, the object pictured (imagined) seems so much smaller than the original (real)
because the various points which correspond to different
points of the original are all crowded together. We see
a whole room pictured in miniature in a convex mirror
that hangs upon the wall (Plate IVA).

When the reflected surface is curved the other way,
the results are of course of the opposite nature (Fig. 14).
The ripples that spread out in circles are reflected
approximately in circles as before: but if the surface is
sufficiently curved they no longer seem to come from a
point behind the mirror. On the contrary they converge

23

upon a point in front. If the dipping point is at the centre of the circular reflector the waves return to that point after reflection, go through it and then diverge from it. If the dipping point is nearer to the surface than its centre, the meeting point or image is further away, and vice versa. So, if we place a bright point at the

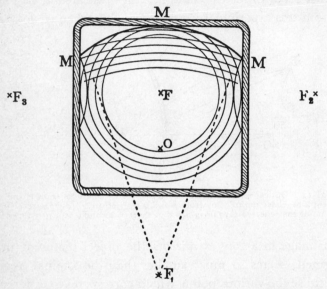

Fig. 14. The reflection of ripples at a concave surface.

centre of a concave mirror, that is to say the centre of the spherical surface of which the mirror is a part, the image of the point is also at the centre: if we move the point inwards the image moves outwards, and vice versa (Fig. 15). Also if we move the point upwards the image moves downwards, and again vice versa. If we place a candle in front of the mirror, the image of the top is depressed, and that of the bottom is raised for the

PLATE IV

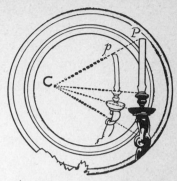

A. Reflection in a convex mirror. The images of the objects in the room where the photograph was taken appear right way up, diminished in size and distorted. The image of the camera is to be seen on the left.

The mirror is part of a spherical surface which has a centre C. A straight line drawn through the middle point of the lens of the camera, and through the image of that point must pass through C, because a ray starting from the lens and going towards C must come straight back again after reflection. Thus C must lie behind the middle point of the image of the lens in the photograph. In the drawing which represents some of the principal features of the photograph, the point C is marked. The dotted lines show that the straight line joining each point in the drawing to its image, for example P to p, goes through C as it ought to do, because the line joining any point to its image must pass through the centre of the lens.

(*p.* 23)

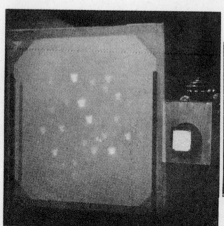

C.

B. A. photograph of an experiment arranged to demonstrate the principle of the pinhole camera. The explanation is given in the text. (*p.* 32)

same reason, so that the candle seems to be upside down: and also its right and left are interchanged.

If the dipping point in the tank is half way between the curved surface and its centre, the waves after reflection have lost nearly all their curvature, and travel outwards in approximately parallel straight lines. They will retain their form and strength for a long time. When

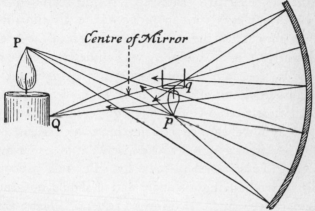

Fig. 15. Optical reflection at a concave mirror.

waves diverge as if from a point behind the mirror they weaken by spreading: and if they converge they pass ultimately through a point from which they diverge and again they weaken. If a ray of light is to be projected a long way, it is best to arrange that in the beginning it neither converges nor diverges. In the case of a circular mirror this is approximately realised when the source of light is in the half way position. But the circular form of mirror is not very successful except when the mirror is small: it is not possible to obtain reflected waves that are quite straight. A parabolic form of reflector is required and the source of light must be at the focus of the parabola.

Seeing

Now let us think a little more about the process of 'seeing.' How do our eyes take in all the details of an object and judge its appearance and position ? The one essential fact is, that when waves of light fall upon any substance, they are scattered. If the scattered rays come to our eyes we can judge of the direction from which they last came. That is one item of news that helps us to 'see.' Moreover, we can determine the distance to a certain extent, basing our estimate on the magnitude of the effort we have to make to see the object clearly. Most of us have to 'screw up' our eyes, as we say, if we want to see something which is close: and to release the eye muscles when we want to see far-away objects. Later we shall see why. But this is not the only way of judging distance: and, I should imagine, a comparatively ineffective way in general. There are at least two others of which we make great use. The first of these is by an estimate of the position of the object relative to other objects. We look, for example, at a small object, a watch let us say, placed upon a table a few yards away. We find that we can judge its position with considerable accuracy: we may be able to estimate approximately the distance from our eyes and the height above the floor. On what do we base this estimate ? In part on a survey which we have made, almost unconsciously, of the object and its surroundings, and on a calculation based on the survey. First of all we 'run our eyes' over the object. The eye can be moved so that the waves scattered from each point of the object in turn are clearly impressed on the most sensitive spot of the retina. We receive different impressions from each point of the object, and these are telegraphed along the nerves that lead to the brain. There, they are collected and examined, and long practice has enabled us to interpret them as due to the scattering of light by a watch. Probably we do not look very carefully at each point: in fact we may be too far away to do so. But we know the general appearance of watches, we may have seen where it came from and had it in view while it was being placed on the table; we put together various facts of this kind: all is done without conscious thinking. Having got so far we proceed with our sub-conscious argument in some such way as this: a floor-space of so many yards separates us from the table, the latter is of the ordinary height and the watch lies in the middle of it. From such observations and arguments we form our idea of the position of the watch. In doing so we are of course making use of the long practice of years.

It is not difficult to convince ourselves that this surveying and estimating are quite important. We put it out of our power to make the survey and we find that it is much harder to tell where the object is. A black ball is hung by a thread which may be visible near the ball, but loses itself higher up, and we do not see the point of suspension. We do not know the size of the ball, and we lose the assistance which formerly we gained by knowing the general size and character of the object. We cover up one eye, for we have not yet discussed the combination

27

of the two eyes which is also important. If then we look at the ball, we find it is not at all easy to tell how far it is away. We shall probably begin to sway the head from side to side, so as to get some idea of how far away the ball is from the wall or ceiling that makes the background, and if we can make out any details in the background and know how far that is away, then we may learn something about the position of the ball. But this is not fair because we have then made a new use of the method of survey and sub-conscious calculation.

We may easily find other cases of the same difficulty of estimating distance, when only one eye is used and the means of survey are not present. If for example we lie under a tree in leaf and look up through the branches – using one eye only – and if we look in such a direction that we cannot learn positions by following the boughs to their point of junction, we find it very hard to say how far one spread of leaves is behind another.

Binocular Vision

Finally we come to the combined use of the two eyes, and find here a very effective method of judging distance which depends on a principle differing entirely from all that we have considered hitherto. The two eyes do not see exactly the same picture: and the brain has learnt by practice how to judge the relative distances of objects by taking account of that difference. The eyes are close together and the difference between the two pictures is very small: it is amazing therefore that the effect produced should be so great. If we compare a pair of stereoscopic photographs such as are illustrated in Plate IIB,

28

we find these small differences everywhere. The subject is a cloister in the church on Mont St. Michel. Observe how the pillars in the background are related to those in the foreground. In the left hand picture the former are more to the left of the latter than they are in the right hand picture: the two pictures have been taken from different points of view, just as they would be seen by two eyes. The stereoscopic camera is an optical device by which each eye is made to see its proper picture, and this gives the illusion of space. The success of this plan shows clearly how effective is the combination of the two eyes in enabling us to judge the distances and the mutual positions of objects. This power is confined to a very limited number of living beings: man possesses it, and perhaps a few other vertebrates. Most animals cannot make use of binocular vision, as we may clearly see from the disposition of their eyes.

Pinhole Images

We have been considering the main principles that govern the reflection and scattering of light from surfaces on which the light waves fall. Let us consider one or two additional illustrations of their application.

When sunshine pierces its way between the leaves of a tree and makes little bright patches of light upon the ground, we notice that they are not angular but rounded: they make a 'dappled shade.' The openings in the tree through which the rays have passed are bounded by the edges of leaves, and are themselves of angular form: clearly they cannot be the determining factors of the shape of the patches on the ground. As a

29

matter of fact these take their form from the sun, and we can see how this must be.

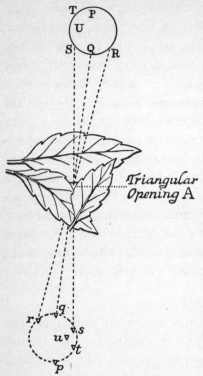

Fig. 16. The upper circle represents the sun and the lower its image upon the ground, due to the passage of sunlight through the triangular opening between the leaves. Each bright point upon the sun makes its own bright triangular patch upon the ground: the sum of all is the circle on the ground, with its penumbra.

Let the upper circle of Fig. 16 represent the sun, and let A be a little aperture in a screen of some sort: it may be the foliage of a tree. From one edge of the sun's disc, marked S, rays stream down through A and fall on the ground at *s*: whence they are scattered. Some of them enter our eyes, and because they are of the sort that come from the sun we imagine that there is at *s* something which sends out rays as the sun does. Rays from Q make an image at *q*, and so for each point on the sun's disc. Thus there is an image of the whole sun upon the ground. The smaller the opening at A, the more perfect the picture. This will be clear if it is first realised that the rays from a single point such as S make upon the ground a patch of light of the same form and size as the opening. The whole patch on the ground may be looked on as an assemblage of these separate patches made by all the points of the sun's disc. In the figure the opening might have the shape of A: then the large patch on the ground would be an assemblage of triangles like A. It is not possible to draw them all, but a few are put into the figure to help the explanation. When the opening is very small compared to the size of the whole patch, the fact that each point on the sun does not make a point upon the ground but a patch of the size of the opening does not have a noticeable effect. Though a small opening does not let through much light, the picture it makes is round like the sun for the reason given. A large opening lets through more light, but the larger it is the more does the patch on the ground lose the round shape of the sun and take that of the opening. The drawing of Fig. 16 will help to make this clear. Only the less brilliant patches look round. The photograph of Plate VA, showing this effect, was taken in a sunny garden. During an eclipse of the sun the patches become crescent-shaped.

Obviously there is no sharp edge to these pictures, because the overlapping pictures of the opening do not add together their effects so well at the edge as in the middle. This half tone effect is called the penumbra, the half shade that separates the full shade from the bright portion of the picture.

It is easy to demonstrate the pinhole effect. In front of a bare arc light is placed a piece of smoked glass, a few inches away. A small hole is made with a pin in the smoke layer, and at once there is a patch of light upon the screen a few feet away, which we recognise as a picture of the burning arc. If a number of small holes of all shapes and sizes are made, each gives rise to the same picture on the screen. Only when the hole is quite large do we find that its form is having any effect upon the shape of the picture.

A photograph of the experiment is shown in Plate IVB. The arc lantern is at the back upon the right and the small bright square is the smoked glass which intercepts the issuing beam of light. It looks white although it is covered with a sooty layer, because it is so brightly lit by the lantern. The holes in the layer are too small to be seen easily in the photograph : an enlargement of the glass is therefore shown in Plate IVc. The screen on which the images are formed is viewed from the back. It will be observed that these images correspond in position with the holes in the screen. Each of them has a double appearance representing the bright terminals of the two carbons : and all of them are alike though the holes vary much in shape.

A pinhole camera operates on this principle; it gives accurate pictures but the exposures must be very long. A quaint illustration of the pinhole effect is given in Plate Vc.

When an object is held in the light of the bare arc, at some distance away from it, and close to the screen, the penumbra is almost invisible, and the outline of the shadow is very sharp.

We take a card cut boldly to show the principal outlines of a face. When it is held before the bare arc it has a bony look. But when the flame of a candle is

PLATE V

A. The photograph taken in a sunny garden shows the shadow of bushes upon a wall. The hand and its shadow show the general disposition. The many small bright circular spots are 'pinhole images' of the sun. (*p. 31*)

B. This figure is taken from Guillemin's *Forces of Nature*. The outlines of a sharply cut card are softened in the shadow by the 'penumbra' effect. (*p. 32*)

C. From a drawing in Guillemin's *Forces of Nature*, illustrating the action of a pinhole camera. (*p. 32*)

PLATE VI

A. Four squares of sateen, cut from the same piece are arranged on a board, so that their threads lie in different directions. The observer has the board in front of him and the light behind him. They appear to be of unequal brightness. (*p.* 33)

B. The reflection from the Japanese 'magic mirror' is thrown upon the lower part of the screen. On the upper part is a photograph of the back of the mirror, projected by a lantern from the back of the theatre. The correspondence between the two pictures is obvious. This is a composite photograph. It is arranged to show the manner of the experiment as well as the result; and in consequence the balance of the tones is wrong. The theatre actually looks brighter than the screen, which is, of course, not the case. (*p.* 35)

substituted for the arc, the penumbra borders the sharp outline and the softer contours give the picture a more natural appearance (Plate VB)

Lustre

Another interesting example of the effects of reflection is to be found in the lustrous effects which some woven materials possess naturally or have impressed upon them. It is not easy to say exactly what we mean by lustre, but it seems to be essential that light shall be reflected when we do not expect it. A lustrous object is not merely a good reflector. If that were so a quick-silvered mirror would be the most lustrous object of all,

Fig. 17. A mode of weaving which gives lustre to the material. Many threads lie parallel to one another giving a wavy form to the surface.

whereas we should all agree, that it has no lustre whatever. We can test this idea of the nature of lustre by a simple experiment. A light from the lantern falls at an angle on a piece of sateen; a coloured sateen is the best for our purpose. The source of light is behind us, and the reflected light from a mirror put in the place of the material would not enter our eyes at all. But if the sateen is turned round in its own plane, each of us sees it flash out for a moment – in fact, for two moments – during each complete revolution. To make this plain, all other lights in the room are turned out. Now, where does the flash come from ? (Plate VIA).

If the material is examined under a magnifying glass,

33

the threads of the warp are seen running parallel to one another. The material is so woven that on one surface of it, the shining side, the threads run over several of the weft threads before dipping under; the illustration (Fig. 17) will help to make this clear. There is therefore a large display on this surface of threads lying even and parallel. Now when the reflected light flashes out in the experiment these threads are perpendicular to the line bisecting the angle made by the two lines joining the material to the light and to our eyes respectively (Fig. 18). The surface is, in fact, furrowed, and

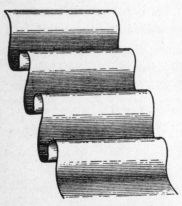

the reflection of the light takes place at the edges of the furrows. Each thread must have a good reflecting surface, of course; apart from that, the effect is obtained by laying them parallel with each other. On the under-side of the material, where there is not such an obvious arrangement in one direction, there is far less lustre. The

Fig. 18. The diagram shows how a rippled material can reflect light in many directions.

regular arrangement of the furrows is clearly at the bottom of the effect. One gets the same effect in a newly ploughed field, where the sides of the furrows are still shiny from the stroking of the plough; and on rippling water when a light shines upon it.

For this reason the furrowing is sometimes intensified by machinery. The material is passed between heated rollers, on which fine parallel grooves have been cut, and this has the desired effect. The process is known as 'schreinering,' being named after its inventor.

The Magic Mirror

Lastly let me draw an illustration from one of the so-called 'magic mirrors' of Japan. It has a very peculiar property. The front is very nearly plane, and does not appear to have any unusual characteristics. On the back is a deeply-marked pattern, which it took from the mould in which it was cast; this is shown in Plate VIB. If the mirror is held in the rays from the lantern, so that the front casts a reflection upon the screen the pattern on the back is contained in the reflection. It looks as if the pattern had shown through, and yet this is obviously impossible because the mirror is of metal of some thickness. It is this curious effect which seemed to those who observed it to be due to magic. There is, however, a very simple explanation which was given by Professor Ayrton in the theatre of the Royal Institution fifty years ago. It depends on the principles we have already been considering: and in fact is an illustration of the laws of reflection from curved surfaces.

Professor Ayrton and his friend Professor Perry once held higy positions in the education system of Japan. Mirrors resembling this magic mirror are very common objects: part of the standard equipment of every lady's dressing room. Ayrton and Perry were very interested to find that a small proportion of the mirrors exhibited the 'magical' property. The property was strange enough in itself: and it was even more strange that no one knew why only one or two mirrors in every hundred possessed it. They made many enquiries; they found that in China much attention had been given to it and that queer explanations had been suggested, none of which they could accept. Finally they arrived themselves at a satisfactory solution: it was suggested by an accidental observation. One of the mirrors had a deep scratch on the back, made by a blunt nail: and they saw that the scratch showed in the picture thrown by the mirror of the front face. They connected this fact with the circumstances of the manufacture of the mirrors. When the

Fig. 19. A Japanese workman polishing the kind of mirror that gives the 'magic' effects. From Silvanus Thompson's *Light Visible and Invisible*, being a portion of a Japanese print in the British Museum.

Japanese workman has cast his mirror, with the pattern on the back, he places it on a board and begins to smooth out the irregularities of the face by the use of a scraper. Fig. 19 shows him hard at it. Whenever he presses on the mirror it bends. He draws stroke after stroke until he has covered the face with a series of parallel movements, and as he does so the thinner parts of the mirror bend and give to the tool more than the thicker parts which lie over the prominences of the pattern. Thus the thinner parts escape to some extent the action of the scraper, and when the pressure has passed they recover and rise slightly above the average level of the face. When the workman has finished one set of parallel scrapings he makes another at right angles to the first and then others in other directions. Finally, the mirror is covered with slight elevations which repeat the pattern on the back: it becomes an assemblage of slightly convex mirrors. When the waves of light are reflected from the face they are not reflected evenly: they converge and diverge and the manner of the disturbance is directly related to the pattern on the back. It seems very strange that so slight a departure from the regularity of the surface should produce an effect so obvious. But perhaps we may compare what we see here with other observations that we have made. When we use the ripple tank the shadows cast on the screen are clear enough: they are due to the bending of the light by the ripples, and yet the ripples themselves are not at all easy to see when we look for them on the surface of the water. Perhaps we have noticed the ripples on the ceiling when water outside the window, or it may be a porthole, is stirred by a very light breeze and reflects the sunshine.

CHAPTER II

THE EYE AND VISION

How Confusion on the Retina is Avoided

WE have seen that light may be considered to be a wave motion which, spreading outwards from its source, is scattered and reflected and, it may be, altered by the various objects which it meets successively. When the light enters the eye it brings news of the source from which it has come, and of its experiences on the way. In particular it tells of the last encounter with a material object before entry into the eye, and so enables the owner of the eye to 'see' that object.

When a confused medley of radiations enters the eye, having come from many sources, and been scattered by many objects, it must be sorted out to become intelligible./ At the back of the eye is the retina, a surface sensitive to light. If each of the sets of waves that enter the eye were spread over the whole of the retina the disentanglement would surely be difficult. There is a device, therefore, which gathers together the waves coming from each and every external point, and converges them upon a corresponding point on the retina. Thus all the details of the view are impressed upon the retina in their proper places relative to one another, and each with its proper character. The whole is then referred to the brain by way of a complicated system of nerves, and is there interpreted. We may say that a picture is formed on the retina, but we must not take the statement too literally. The act of vision does not require the formation of a small picture in the eye, correct in colour and detail, upon a background like a piece of white paper or the ground glass of a photographic camera. It is sometimes imagined that such a picture is actually made and is then regarded by some sensory organ, as we look at a picture on the wall.

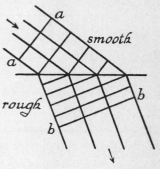

In order to effect the sorting of the medley of radiations advantage is taken of the fact that light travels in different media with different velocities. Light travels in glass for example, at about two thirds of its velocity in

Fig. 20. The line *a a* and the others that are parallel to it represent ranks marching on the smooth ground. On entering upon the rough ground the ranks are swung round and become parallel to *b b*. They also close up.

air: in water, at about three quarters. Now, if an advancing wave enters a medium in which it moves more slowly, and if it strikes the surface of separation obliquely, it swings round, because one part of the wave is checked before the other. A very familiar example of this change of direction is to be seen on the sea-shore, where the waves, as they roll in, always break in lines that are parallel to the beach, whatever the direction in which they have been moving further out to sea. Their speed grows less as they enter the shallowing water, and so those parts of the wave system which are ahead of the rest are held back until the alignment is complete and follows the contour lines of the beach.

In the same way soldiers on the march are apt to be deflected from their proper direction if they strike, obliquely to their ranks, a patch of ground where walking is more difficult (Fig. 20).

An actual experiment will illustrate the point. A

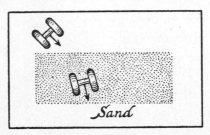

Fig. 21.   The dotted portion of the diagram represents sand spread upon a table.   The pair of freely running wheels is rolled towards the sanded area and swings round on reaching it.

pair of wheels running freely on a common axle may be set in motion upon a board, so as to come obliquely upon a sandy patch where motion is more difficult. The wheel that strikes first is held back, and the direction of the movement is changed so as to become more nearly at right angles to the line where the sand begins. (Fig. 21).

It is not difficult to see now how a set of advancing waves may be made to converge upon a point. It is only necessary to arrange that the centre of the advance shall be obliged to cross some space where the motion is slowed down, while the wings are allowed to run on. If this space is correctly outlined the waves then take a crescent shape, and as all parts of a wave move forward in a direction perpendicular to their own particular section of the front, the motion gradually converges upon a point and piles up its energy there. Such a point is called a focus. The waves pass through this point and diverge again in ever widening circles.

The effect may be illustrated upon the ripple tank. A sheet of glass is cut so that its outline is that of the

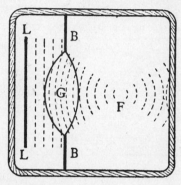

Fig. 22.   The ripple tank is seen from above.   A sheet of glass G cut in the form of a section of a lens is laid on the floor of the tank, diminishing the depth of the water which is usually about a quarter of an inch.   The ripples travel more slowly in the shallow water.   Thus they are made to converge upon a point F: after passing through F they diverge.   The ripples are started by a lath L which dips in and out: the barriers B B prevent the ripples from passing by the sides of the lens.

section of a lens, and is laid upon the floor of the tank. The water above it is more shallow than elsewhere, and waves when they cross it move more slowly. Waves can be set in motion by a wooden lath parallel to the surface of the water which vibrates at the end of a spring and dips in and out of the water continuously. The converging process is obvious: though it is far from being as definite as in the case of light (Fig. 22. See also Plate VIIA).

When therefore, a glass lens is placed in the path of an

advancing train of light waves, the thicker central portions of the lens check the waves more than the outlying thinner parts, and the light is brought to a focus, through which it passes and begins to spread again. The effect is shown by the simple experiment of Fig. 23 and indeed is very familiar to us all.

The water tank analogy gives an idea of the nature of the process, but unless something more is said, it may leave a misleading impression that the action of a lens upon a ray of light is lacking in precision. The very

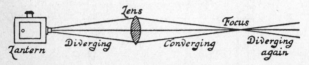

Fig. 23. This diagram shows the action of a lens. The rays from the lantern are made to converge upon a focus from which they afterwards diverge.

contrary is the case. Rays of light emanating from a point source can be brought to an extremely sharp focus if the lens is properly designed and constructed. That is because the waves of light are very short in comparison with the dimensions of the lens. In every inch of the train there are tens of thousands of waves, and when this is the case the train moves forwards with very little spreading. When directed to a particular point there is extremely little wandering from the path that has been set. The fact is an example of a general law of the greatest importance, of which we shall see other examples from time to time. So minute are the waves that the very highest technical skill, on the part of the glass worker and the lens grinder, is required to take full advantage of the opportunities given to them. There is,

42

indeed, a limit to what can be done, but it is not reached
until the work is on so fine a scale that the very molecules
of the glass must be regarded as separate bodies. The
glass of a lens of high quality must be homogeneous
throughout, a matter of great difficulty if the dimensions
are of any magnitude: the calculation of the form is an
intricate matter, and the grinding must conform to it to

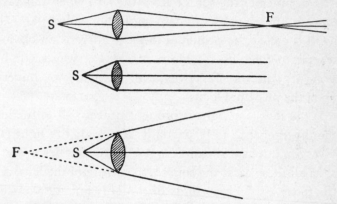

Fig. 24. These diagrams show the converging action of the lens for various
relative positions of lens and source.

a hair's breadth and less. There are, of course, many
ordinary purposes which do not exact so much from the
skill of the optician.

If we make the source of light approach the lens, the
focus recedes. This is entirely in accordance with the
view we have formed of the way in which the convergence is brought about. The lens checks by a definite amount the motion of the waves that pass through
its centre, and this amount effects a certain change in the
form of the wave, causing it to converge when previously
it diverged. Clearly, the greater the previous divergence

the less will be the convergence which is substituted for it, as Figs. 23 and 24 show. If in fact, the source is brought sufficiently near the lens, the waves will not diverge at all after passing through. All that the lens has been able to do is to destroy their previous divergence, so that they now become plane waves, and travel without further divergence or convergence to a focus. The distance of the source from the lens when this takes place is known as the 'focal length' of the lens, and the point is called the principal focus. There is an obvious reverse to this effect. Plane waves, i.e. waves coming from a point very far away, will be made to converge upon the principal focus.

If the source of light is brought nearer still to the lens the divergence is only partially removed: the light still diverges, but as if it came from a source further away.

In all these cases the source, the centre of the lens, and the focus are in a straight line. This follows from the fact that the lens, at its middle point, behaves like a piece of plate glass; a ray going through the centre is not bent.

The various operations which are illustrated in this series of sketches, operations which we can easily carry out upon the lecture table, can only be approximately successful. A lens can be designed to bring to a focus at any point with great exactness the rays that originate at another point: but it must be designed for those two points. It is not to be expected that the focusing will be equally exact if the distance between those points is altered in the way that we have been doing. A lens that is to function over a considerable range will not be very accurate over the whole of it. In general that is good enough. The experiments described above can be carried out with a comparatively imperfect lens. It is a different matter when the microscope or the telescope or the camera have to be designed for specific and closely defined tasks of great difficulty. Every photographer knows what a wide difference exists between an ordinary camera lens and the best of its kind.

The Image Formed by a Lens

Now that we see how the rays emanating from a point on one side of a lens can be brought to a focus at a point on the other side, we can understand how a lens can form an image upon a screen.

Consider for example the photograph reproduced in Plate VIIB showing the image of an electric lamp. The lens seen edgeways in the centre of the picture brings the rays from the lamp on the right to a focus upon the screen on the left. Rays which come from each separate point of the glowing filament and pass through the lens are made to converge at a point upon the screen. The positions of lens and screen are adjusted for this purpose. The two points are in line with the centre of the lens. After striking the screen at p the rays which came originally from P are scattered again, and an eye that received a portion is affected as if there were at p a source like P. As there is a corresponding image for every point of the original, the whole of the latter appears as an image upon the screen. It is inverted: its size depends on the relative distances of the filament and its image from the screen.

This principle is used in many optical arrangements,

for instance, the photographic camera. In this case the sensitive plate replaces the screen of Plate VII B; it is, of course, sheltered from any extraneous light by the body of the camera. The image of external objects is formed, inverted and much diminished, on the plate.

The Optical Arrangement of the Eye

The optical arrangements of the eye resemble in principle those of the photographic camera. The lens-

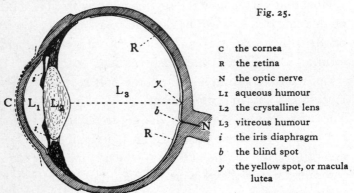

Fig. 25.

c   the cornea
R   the retina
N   the optic nerve
L1 aqueous humour
L2 the crystalline lens
L3 vitreous humour
i   the iris diaphragm
b   the blind spot
y   the yellow spot, or macula lutea

shaped mass L_2 (Fig. 25) and the humours L_1 and L_3 that fill the spaces before and behind the lens all reduce the speed of light as it passes through them, L_2 more than the others, and do so more in the centre than at the edges of the eye. Thus, as before, the diverging waves that meet the eye are made to converge upon the retina, which corresponds to the screen of the camera. Here also the image of an external object which is formed upon the retina is very much smaller than the original and is upside down.

The position of the screen in the photographic camera

PLATE VII

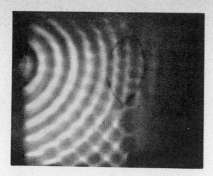

A. This photograph shows the converse effect of that illustrated by Fig. 22. Ripples are started from a point on the left, and pass over a glass sheet cut in the form of a lens. They diverge from the point, but the lens destroys the convergence; on the right of the picture the ripples have become rectilinear. The point is at the principal focus of the lens. The photograph was obtained by a time exposure, during which flashes of light lit up the ripples in time with the movement of the dipper which started them. (*p.* 41)

B. This photograph shows on the left the inverted image of a filament lamp which stands upon the right; the image is produced by the lens in between. The square screen in front of the filament lamp was put there during part of the time while the photograph was being taken in order to cut down the light from the filament, which otherwise would have been too strong for the photographic plate. The inverted image of the filament on the screen is due to the original filament itself; but the inverted shadow of the lamp bulb is due to a light which was placed on the right, out of the field of the photograph. The same external light casts a shadow of the lens and stand which are right way up, because the rays have not been through the lens. (*p.* 45)

C. The two sides of a patch, though its shade is uniform, look a little different. That which is next a darker patch seems to be lighter than that which is next a lighter. The patches consequently have a fluted appearance. (*p.* 61)

is capable of adjustment. This is necessary because the focus of the rays from a distant point is nearer to the lens than that of the rays from a point close to. We are familiar with the sight of the photographer adjusting the position of his plate to suit the distance of his subject.

We have the power, as we know, of observing the details of objects at various distances, and our eyes must therefore possess means of adjustment like the photographic camera. These are provided by muscles which can alter the shape of the eye and its lens system. When we wish to read small print, for example, we are conscious of an effort to contract the muscles about the eye: sometimes we find ourselves frowning in doing so. In this way we make the eye generally, and the eye lens in particular, thicker from back to front and less from side to side. Thus the converging power is increased. Most of us can contract our eyes until we can see objects that are no further away than six to eight inches, but if we bring the objects still closer, our vision is blurred. The nearer we can bring objects to our eyes, without causing blurring, the larger the picture on the retina, and the more we can distinguish the details of what we are looking at.

Optical Defects of the Eye, and Remedies

The normal eye can often make out the separate twigs on a tree fifty yards away when outlined against the sky and can also be adjusted to see fine details a few inches away. Such feats give an idea of the fineness of construction which enables minute objects to be separately brought to a focus on the retina. Yet we know that all eyes are not equally efficient: some can do better at short distances, some at long. Some cannot see objects clearly wherever they are. These defects from the normal are easily explained by a few experiments.

We set up an apparatus to represent the process of vision. The large flask in the figure is filled with a liquid containing a certain amount of suspended matter which allows the track of light rays to be followed

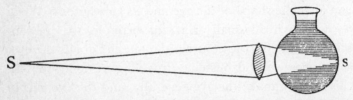

Fig. 26. The rays from an arc at s are brought to a focus by the lens and the liquid in the flask. The focus is situated on the back of the flask. The lens and the liquid represent roughly the optical system of the eye: and the back of the flask represents the retina.

easily. At S is a bare electric arc or a 'pointolite' which provides a sufficiently concentrated source of light. Just in front of the flask is a lens, so chosen that the light from the lamp is brought to a focus on the back of the flask. (Fig. 26.)

The flask of liquid and the lens may be taken to represent roughly the spherical eye ball and the eye lens (Fig. 25): the retina is represented by the back of the flask, and the rays that are focused there in the first arrangement of our experiment correspond to light which enters a normal eye and is focused on the retina. The rays from a point are brought to a point. As we have seen already this is an important matter since in this way the information to be derived from the rays is interpreted without confusion caused by rays coming from other points and falling on the same place.

If the source S is moved, up or down or to right or left, the image s moves also, but down or up or to left or right. In fact there is the inversion that we have already seen to be a necessary accompaniment of the lens action. The 'picture' formed on the retina is upside down. Why then it may be asked do we not see objects

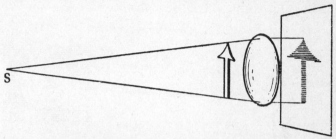

Fig. 27. A source of light s throws a shadow of an object upon a screen close to it. The interposition of a lens – of not too short a focus – between the object and the screen does not make much difference to the shadow, merely causing slight reduction and blurring.

upside down ? Because when we first began to interpret the sensations in our eyes we learnt how to distinguish high from low, the top part of an object from the bottom. But we never knew how this was done; we were content to learn by experiment. Most people are unaware that the retina picture is upside down: they have never met with any actual evidence that it is so. Unless they have observed the action of a lens and realised the function of the lens system of the eye, the reality will not have occurred to them.

It is possible to demonstrate the effect by simple experiments.[1] In the first place we place a lens a little

[1] Silvanus Thompson, *Light Visible and Invisible*, p. 44.

distance away from a screen as in Fig. 27; and place some simple object close to the lens. It is then observed that the lens does not interfere with the casting of a shadow of the object upon the screen: and the shadow is right way up.

Let the observer prick a hole in a card and, bringing the card close to the eye, look through the hole at a bright surface, the sky or a bright lamp shade (Fig. 28).

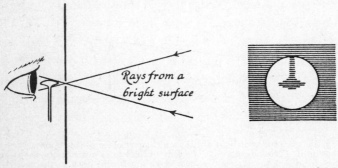

Rays from a bright surface

Figs. 28 and 29. The eye is placed close to the small hole in the card. Light from a bright surface, e.g. the sky, comes through the hole and floods the retina so that the hole looks large. If a pin and pin-head are placed between the hole and the eye, as in the figure, the shadow on the retina must be right way up in accordance with the previous experiment. But the appearance is as shown in the second of the two figures in this diagram: the pin seems to be wrong way up.

Quite a considerable bright circle will appear to the eye, because a considerable area of the retina will be illuminated. The fact is that the lens is unable to bring to a point the rays that diverge so widely after passing through the small hole. Now let the pin be held so that the head comes between the hole and the eye. It may require a little time to get it into place. The shadow on the retina must be right way up (Fig. 27), but the interpretation of the brain will be that it is upside down. What the eye 'sees' is shown in Fig. 29.

It may be pointed out that the image on the retina differs from the original not only in being inverted but also in being greatly diminished. There is no more reason for supposing that we ought to see things upside down than for supposing that we ought to see them much smaller than they really are.

If in the experiment of Fig. 26 we move the source of light S further away from the model eye, the rays are brought to a focus before they get to the retina and have begun to spread again when they arrive there. If the source S is made to approach the eye, the rays have not met in a focus by the time they get to the retina. In either case the image is blurred. The same effect must occur in the use of the eye unless some arrangement is introduced to avoid it. The lens and its accompanying optical devices can be modified by the action of the various eye muscles, and vision can be adjusted to circumstances within certain limits. This power of adaptation of various eyes differs greatly. The normal eye can be adjusted so that, on the one hand, the details of a landscape can be seen with marvellous clearness already referred to, and on the other, a book can be read comfortably at about ten inches away. But some eyes are so made that distant objects appear in a haze: only those that are close to can be clearly seen. Such short-sighted eyes may be assisted by lenses which are thinner in the centre than at the edges: these are known as concave lenses. Since the eyes converge the waves too much, they must be corrected by lenses which open the rays out by providing a greater check at the edges than at the centre. Conversely the eyes that cannot converge the waves enough must be provided with lenses that are convex, that is to say thicker at the centre. Very many people find as they grow old that such lenses become necessary, because the lens of the eye grows flatter with the years (Figs. 30 and 31).

Fig. 30.

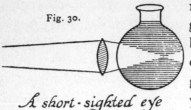

A short-sighted eye

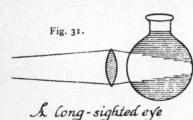

can be aided by a concave lens

Fig. 31.

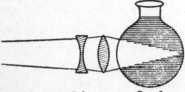

A long-sighted eye

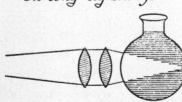

can be aided by a convex lens

Figs. 30 and 31. These diagrams show how eyes that are too long-sighted and too short-sighted are corrected for their defects.

Magnification

The larger the picture on the retina the easier it is to make out the details of the original, provided that each point of the original is brought sharply to focus. To make the picture as large as possible the original must be brought as close as possible to the eye: the limit is set by the power of the eye system to alter the divergence of the rays and bring about such a convergence that the focus is on the retina. If we wish to examine an object closely we bring it as close to our eyes as we can, but, as we know, we have to stop short at a point which is pretty definite. That is the point where the power of the eye system begins to fail. There is no use in bringing the object still closer: the picture will grow, but the details will become obscure. In order to get over this difficulty it is customary to make use of a lens which adds to the converging power of the eye: the ordinary magnifying glass in its various forms. With such a lens (Fig. 32)

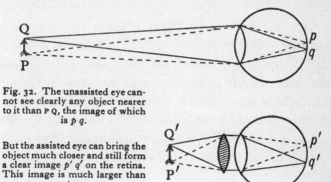

Fig. 32. The unassisted eye cannot see clearly any object nearer to it than P Q, the image of which is *p q*.

But the assisted eye can bring the object much closer and still form a clear image *p′ q′* on the retina. This image is much larger than *p q*.

the object may be brought much closer and clearness is not sacrificed to magnification. The ordinary reading glass which we pick up in order to see fine print or the details of a picture does not magnify very much, and its construction does not require an excessive care. The higher the magnification that is required, the greater is the claim upon the skill of the lens maker: good work is required for the construction of the lens that is used by the botanist or geologist, or the watchmaker. Moreover, there is a limit to the method itself, in spite of the lens maker's skill. The object to be examined cannot in all cases be brought sufficiently close to the eye to give the magnification that is urgently required. A very different method is employed therefore.

The Microscope and Telescope

We may pause to remind ourselves how very much these matters mean to us. On either side of those magnitudes which our eyes can see and examine unaided are wide ranges of magnitudes which are outside ordinary vision. It is of course true that lives could be lived without spectacles, magnifying glasses, microscopes, or telescopes. But it is also true that without them we should know nothing of all that life, friendly and unfriendly, which is bound up in the very small, and which affects us so closely. We should know no more of the stars than that they were bright points in the sky. In fact, we should be unaware of untold riches in the ordering of the world, and of the universe of which it is part.

In the new method we first make an image of that which is to be examined, and then apply our magnifying glass to that image. By so doing we gain in two ways: in the first place we can make the image much larger than the original, and in the second place we can get at it more easily. Suppose for example, that a small object PQ (Fig. 33), is placed close to a lens L and is brightly illuminated. An enlarged image is formed on a screen SS. The illumination must be strong so that the image may be sufficiently bright even when so greatly enlarged. We may now apply our magnifying glass to this image. We could receive the image on a white screen at SS and look at it from the front. But it is infinitely better to look at the picture from the back using a lens as in Fig 32 : the screen is not wanted then because the rays from any point in the original will be brought to a focus at a point where the screen was, and will then diverge and enter the eye as shown in the figure. Moreover, in this way the whole of the light goes to the eye, whereas the screen scatters it.

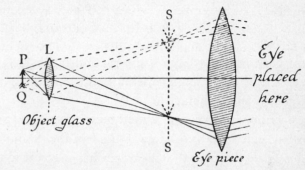

Fig. 33. The plan of the microscope. The brightly illuminated object P Q, scatters rays of light from which the lens L, called the object glass, forms an image at s s, much larger than the object. This is examined by a second lens called the eyepiece in the manner of the previous drawing, Fig. 32.

This is the principle of the microscope. There are two essentials in the optical system, Fig. 33, first the object glass which makes the enlarged image, and secondly, the eyepiece by which it is examined. The magnifying power of a microscope depends on the construction of both these parts. And again it must be said that if the best results are to be obtained a very high degree of craftsmanship is required.

When it is desired to aid the eye to see the details of a more distant object a similar arrangement is made. In this case, however, the object glass cannot be placed near to the object, and therefore the image which it makes cannot be an enlargement. An image is made however, and the eyepiece or magnifying lens can help the eye to do far better by examining the image than the eye could do unaided.

The greater the focal length of the object glass, the larger the first image: for which reason a powerful astronomical telescope is of great length. But then the question of illumination becomes important: since the light that comes through the object glass has to be spread over the whole of the image. Therefore, the object glass must be large if the magnification is large, and it is here that the expense of construction begins to limit what can be achieved.

It may be well to repeat a method of approach to this question which we have already used in the case of the microscope. Suppose that a camera has been set to take a photograph. If we look at the ground glass screen before a sensitive plate has been put in its place, having arranged a black cloth to keep out extraneous light, we see a picture of the scene upside down. To this we might apply a magnifying lens so as to bring out the details. But having got the lens into position, it is clear that we shall do ever so much better if we take the screen away. The rays that were received at a point on the plate and were scattered in all directions now pass straight on into the eyepiece without being weakened by dispersion.

Thus, to sum up, there are three stages in the advancement of powers of vision. In the first we use our unaided eyes: in the next, which applies only to the case of minute objects which we can approach nearly, we use a lens or magnifying glass to help our eyes: in the third, we first make an image of the object by the use of an object glass, and then apply our eyepiece or magnifying glass to the image. All microscopes and telescopes are built on this principle, however they vary in detail. Great ingenuity has been spent on the design of instruments for special purposes, as for example, on the modern binoculars. The consideration of such instruments is outside our present purpose.

Astigmatism

It is a familiar fact that the eyes of different persons vary widely in their power of clear vision. Some of us cannot distinguish details at a distance, others find it difficult to read a book. We repair our deficiencies by using spectacles of proper design. There is no standard eye, adapted to the requirements of the average man. Since there is such variation in this respect, so great that we are frequently in need of artificial help to adjust our eyes to vision at useful distances, it is not surprising that in other respects eyes sometimes fail to conform to the normal, and in particular to the symmetrical form which may be taken as normal. If the rays from a point source on the axis of a lens are to be brought to a point, the lens must be symmetrical about the axis. It is easy to see what happens when this is not the case. We take a lens which has been ground so that its curvature in the upright direction A B is less than the curvature in the horizontal direction C D. We find that the light from the point source cannot be brought to a point on the far side of the lens. The stronger curvature of the horizontal section of the lens converges the rays at the sides more quickly than they are converged in the vertical plane. The result is as shown in Fig. 34.

At one point the rays all pass through a short vertical line: they all pass through a horizontal line a little further on. In between they are all compassed by a small circle. But they never pass through a point, for which reason the effect is known as astigmatism. No object near

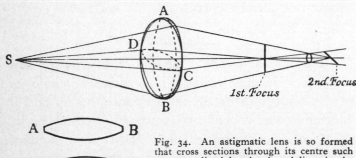

Fig. 34. An astigmatic lens is so formed that cross sections through its centre such as are outlined by the dotted lines in the figure are not all alike. For instance, the faces of the section D C are more curved than those of A B. The rays from s after passing through the lens do not converge upon a point, but upon two short line foci, as shown in the figure. The first line is in the plane of the diagram, the second is perpendicular to it.

or far can be seen clearly by an eye subject to this defect. Fortunately it is easy to devise and construct lenses which can counteract it. The astigmatic eye must have one direction of greatest curvature, and one of least, which need not of course be the vertical and horizontal directions (Fig. 34). A lens which reverses this difference will correct the fault. To an astigmatic eye lines on a piece of paper are best seen when drawn in certain directions. Such an eye looking at the diagram of Fig. 35 may see the vertical lines more plainly than the horizontal, or vice versa: or may observe a difference at some moment while the page is slowly turned round in its own plane. This may be explained in the following way.

Let us suppose that the lens of the eye is of the type shown in Fig. 34, and that the rays of light from a point source after passing through it converge first of all upon a short vertical line upon the retina. Each point upon a vertical line upon which the eye is gazing will

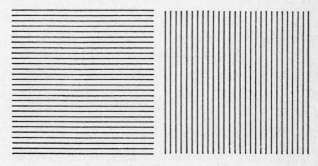

Fig. 35. A test for astigmatism of the eye.

be drawn out on the retina into a short vertical line, and all these will overlap so as to make on the whole a line which is clear. But if the line on the paper is horizontal, and each point upon it is drawn out into a vertical line, the result is a hazy horizontal line.

Mistakes of Interpretation

In the foregoing pages we have been considering the eye as an optical instrument by which a picture of external objects is formed on the back of the retina: and we have examined various cases of the failure of the instrument to function. We have also seen that the interpretation of this picture contributes to a sub-conscious process by which the brain recognises the details of the scene. Just as there may be faults in the optical system, so also there may be faults in the interpretation due to want of experience, or to carelessness, or less avoidably, to the nature of the physiological processes by which the light is transformed into the nervous impulses, and these again into sensation. For example,

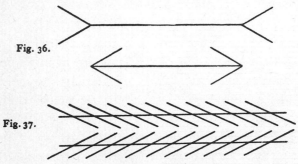

Fig. 36.

Fig. 37.

Figs. 36 and 37. Two well known illusions. In the upper figure are the horizontal lines equal ? In the lower figure are the long lines parallel to each other ?

I would suggest that the well known illusion of the relative length of the horizontal lines (Fig. 36) is largely a matter of not taking trouble. The lower line looks the smaller because the eye locates its end somewhere in the arrow head and does not follow it to the tip. A practised draughtsman is not misled in this way, nor does he make the mistake of thinking that the two lines of Fig. 37 are inclined to one another, though a hasty glance may give rise to the illusion.

On the other hand, when a dark patch is contiguous with one that is lighter there is an illusion that the light patch is still lighter in that part of it which lies close to the dark, while the darkness of the other patch is enhanced close to the light. The peculiarity of each is 'thrown up,' to use a commonplace phrase, by the presence of the other. In consequence the set of patches shown in Plate VIIᴏ assumes a fluted appearance. Here there may be more than one cause at work: and I am not sure that their relative influences have been satisfactorily determined. One of the most effective is discussed by Shelford Bidwell in *Curiosities of Light and Sight*, viz., the unconscious variation of standard. The eye after regarding the dark patch is more impressed by light than it should be: its standard of brightness is temporarily lowered. This heightening by contrast may also be due in part to a certain physiological effect, namely, the actual fatigue of the retina caused by the incidence of the light which it is made to detect.

As we gaze at the picture our eyes keep wandering from point to point of it. If we look at one of the patches of medium tone just after looking at a brighter patch we do so with eyes slightly fatigued: if after looking at a darker patch, with eyes that are rested. The patch may look darker in the former case than in the latter. Nevertheless, whether fatigue has anything to do with the effect or not, the variation of standard is a certain cause, because the fluted appearance, according to Bidwell, 'is equally well shown when the diagram is illuminated instantaneously by the electric spark.'

A curious effect of the same kind was shown many years ago at a lecture given in the Royal Institution by Professor William Stirling: his diagram is given in

Plate VIIIA. The white bands seem darker at their places of intersection. It may be supposed that a point in a white band well away from an intersection is surrounded by more black and therefore looks brighter than a point in one of the squares where bands intersect.

One of the most famous of illusions is the apparent enlargement of the moon when near the horizon. It is difficult to believe, when it rises a clear red disc against which distant trees or buildings stand in sharp outline, that it is no larger than when it is overhead. However, the fact is easily verified: a halfpenny at a distance of nine feet just obscures the moon whether on the horizon or high in the zenith. It is of course obvious that the angle subtended by the moon at the eye must always be the same since its distance does not alter. Atmospheric refraction, which we shall consider later, has only a very slight effect upon that angle, and indeed, it causes a small diminution of the horizon size. The illusion is not due therefore to any change in the size of the image upon the retina: nor indeed to any fault of the eye. It must be an error of interpretation. There does not seem to be any reason for doubting an explanation often offered, that the cause is another example of a change of standard. Unconsciously we adopt a different scale for the measurement of objects in the sky, according to their distance from the zenith overhead. We see clouds floating towards the horizon and shrinking in their apparent dimensions while they do so. An aeroplane becomes smaller and smaller as it moves away, the subtended angle decreasing continuously, and it is a mere speck when it disappears behind a distant hill. But the

PLATE VIII

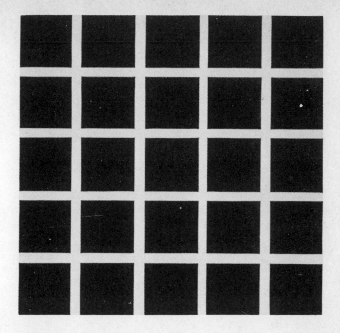

A. Where the white lanes meet in the diagram, there is an illusion of flickering shadows. (*p.* 62)

B. A photograph of an experimental arrangement showing the refraction of a beam of light as it crosses a surface between water and air. (*p.* 68)

PLATE IX

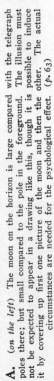

A. (*on the left*) The moon on the horizon is large compared with the telegraph poles there; but small compared to the pole in the foreground. The illusion must not be expected to appear in a drawing like this, though it is possible to induce it by covering up first one picture of the moon and then the other. The actual circumstances are needed for the psychological effect. (*p.* 63)

B. (*on the right*) The moon in this cloud photograph is not easily found. It is a small crescent at equal distances from either side of the photograph, and nearer the top than the bottom. As the moon subtends an angle of half a degree, its size in the picture should be the hundred and twentieth part, approximately, of the focal length of the camera lens, this being the ratio between the size of an object and its distance when subtending an angle of that magnitude. (*p.* 64) moon does not change its subtended angle in this way, and when we see it close to the horizon we measure it on the scale which we have learnt to associate with that part of the sky: and so it looks enormous. If we saw an aeroplane rising above the horizon from behind a distant village, having the same size as when overhead, it would seem to be larger than the village itself, and would surely be a terrifying spectacle. And yet that is what the moon does: so that there is nothing surprising in the fact that it may look large, in spite of all our experience of its behaviour and of our knowledge that it cannot really be any larger there than when it is overhead. The argument is illustrated in Plate IXA.

The representation of the moon in a picture is generally far larger than it should be on geometrical principles. It may be that since no pigment can represent its brilliancy and importance, the painter therefore increases its apparent size in order to give it due importance. Whether or no he is justified in doing so is a question of artistic intention with which we have nothing to do. If a picture is supposed to give objects their true size when held at convenient arm's length, it would be right to give the moon a diameter of nearly one fifth of an inch: if any other distance is supposed to be that at which the picture should be looked at, the size of the painted moon must be altered accordingly.

It is to be remembered that wherever the observer stands the moon subtends the same angle at his eye, whereas every other object in the picture changes its apparent size if the observer shifts his position. On the other hand, from the geometrical standpoint, the size of the moon in the picture depends on how far the picture is held from the eye. In a photograph it depends on the distance of the lens from the plate. A somewhat startling illustration is given in Plate IXʙ.

There is another type of illusion with which we are all, no doubt, familiar, namely the apparent enlargement of distance in a photograph. When we see a photograph of a room that we know, we are at once struck by the fact that it appears much deeper than we think it ought to be.

Geometrically speaking, the photograph cannot lie: the effect cannot be ascribed to distortion due to the use of a lens. It must again be due to mistaken interpretation, and in particular to the unconscious use of a false standard. We are so accustomed to find that distant objects are larger than their apparent size, that we adopt a different scale when we look at them or think of them. A beginner, drawing a landscape, makes the distant hills anything up to ten times their proper height. Conversely, when the details of a room are shown in correct geometrical form, in fact in the form in which they are rendered on the retina, we overestimate the distance of the details at the further end.

There is an illusion of motion which also is due to the use of a false standard. If we sit for some time in the train watching the landscape slide past the windows, our eyes become accustomed to the motion and take it to be a normal condition. If the train stops there is a temporary illusion that the landscape is moving forwards, or the train backwards. A simple experiment due to Shelford Bidwell (see Fig. 38) shows the effect very well.   A lantern slide is made of a square plate of metal in which a vertical slot has been cut.   A spiral slot is cut in a plate which can be made to revolve about an axis which is perpendicular to the first plate.   When the combination is placed in the lantern a bright spot is thrown upon the screen by the white light passing

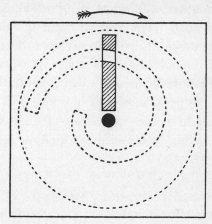

Fig. 38.   The spiral slot is cut in a plate which revolves in front of the lantern: the straight slot in a plate which remains at rest. The purpose of the arrangement is explained in the text.   Bid-well's *Curiosities of Light and Sight*, p. 147.

through the intersection of the two slots, the rest of the field being dark.   The revolution of the second plate causes the spot to travel up the screen and disappear at the top: at the same moment another spot appears at the bottom and commences its travel upwards.   Thus a succession of spots is continuously on the move.   After this has been going on for a quarter of a minute or so, the motion is arrested.   It then seems to the watching eye that the spot is travelling downwards, and the illusion is maintained for several seconds.   Such effects as these are not to be ascribed to any failure of the optical mechanism of the eye: they have to do with interpretation by the brain. Others will doubtless occur to those who have noticed them. There is, for instance, an illusion which the motorist sometimes experiences. When the country over which he is driving is rising gradually to distant mountains he is apt to be mistaken about the levels of the road. He overestimates the slope of the hills he runs down and underestimates those which he climbs. On the other hand, when he is travelling in the opposite direction, he is apt to plume himself without warrant on the performance of his car. The error here is due simply to misinterpretation of observation: it is rectified by taking better account of circumstances.

Persistence of Vision

The phenomenon known as persistence of vision is of a different type, for it is due to particular features of the eye structure which cannot be altered. An impression made upon the retina continues to be registered for a fraction of a second after the cause has ceased to act. Tyndall demonstrated the effect in a very simple way. The lantern projects a cone of light: a white stick is made to cross the cone quickly as if it were a sword slashing the light. The watching eye does not see the stick as it cuts through; it sees a white disc, such as would be produced, but more intensely, if a white screen were placed so as to intercept the light. The eye sees the disc in all its positions at the same moment. If an object such as a watch chain is whirled round in the light from an electric lamp fed with alternating current the bright reflections from the links show the chain in a number of successive positions. The smooth working of the cinema film depends on the persistence of each impression for a reasonable time.

General Instances of Refraction

We have been considering the phenomenon of the refraction of light in relation to the natural optical system of the eye and to such artificial optical systems as

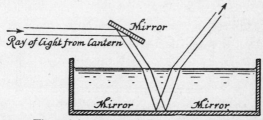

Fig. 39. The tank in the figure is filled with a slightly coloured liquid: and the front of the tank is made of glass, so that the path of the ray can be followed. A mirror forms the bottom of the tank.

the microscope and telescope. Many familiar effects also depend upon refraction, and afford useful and interesting examples of its consequences.

We remember that it occurs whenever waves pass from one medium to another if the velocity of the wave motion is different in the two media. Let us first examine the phenomenon with the aid of a few simple experiments.

In the experiment of Figs. 39 and 40, a pencil of light is directed upon a mirror which deflects it downwards so that it enters the water in a tank. The water is tinged with a dye which makes the path of the ray visible, and one side of the tank is made of glass so that we can see what goes on within. A mirror is laid on the bottom of the tank, so that the ray is reflected, passes through the water of the tank once more and emerges into the open. The bending of the ray as it enters and leaves is easily observed : and we may see also that if the entrance is made more obliquely the angle of bending becomes greater. We may see also that the ray which is reflected from the mirror lying on the floor of the tank returns by a path which is symmetrical with that by which it entered. In

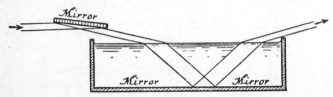

Fig. 40. This figure shows the path of a ray entering the water more obliquely than in Fig. 39.

particular, the ray which almost skims the surface before it enters, skims it just as closely on leaving.

This illustrates one important point, namely that the path of a ray of light is reversible. If we place a mirror fair and square in the path of a ray of light, it goes back by the way it came, taking its reflections and refractions in the reverse order. It gives an idea, also, of the amount of the bending when a ray of light enters water, and shows the considerable increase in the amount when the obliquity is made greater. The refraction effect is demonstrated in Plate VIIIв.

The ray of light that enters the room through the window is diverted from its original course while it is in the glass, but its direction is restored on emergence. Thus there is very little effect on the appearance of objects outside. An experiment on the ripple tank shows clearly how this happens. A strip of glass with parallel sides is laid on the floor of the tank: waves are generated in the usual way. While crossing the shallow water the wave front is temporarily put out of alignment but recovers itself after the crossing. This effect is shown in Plate XA and in Fig. 41. A good piece of window

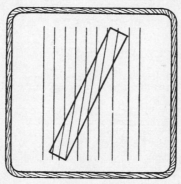

Fig. 41. A rectangular sheet of glass is laid in the ripple tank, and waves sent across it. The temporary change of alignment is rectified as soon as the ripples get across. This shows why the direction of a ray of light is not altered by a sheet of glass with plane parallel sides.

glass does no more therefore than shift rays of light slightly to one side without altering their direction, and this escapes detection. When, however, the two faces of a piece of glass are not parallel, objects seen through the glass appear distorted: an effect which is common enough in the case of glass of inferior quality.

We are now in a position to explain a well known effect. When we look down into water and can see the bottom the depth always appears less than it really is. The eye judges the distance of an object by estimating the position of the point from which the rays seem to diverge.

Owing to the bending of the rays on emergence the eye
is deceived as is shown in Figs. 42 and 43. To the eye
looking vertically downwards into water the apparent

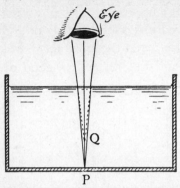

Fig. 42. The rectangular outline is the section of a tank of water. An eye
looks at an object P at the bottom of the tank immediately below. Owing to
refraction the pencil of rays from P which enters the eye is opened out on
leaving the water and seems to come from Q. The eye has to be drawn out
of proportion so that the spreading of the pencil can be shown. The depth
of Q is three-quarters of the depth of the water.

depth is three quarters of the true. The apparent
shallowing is greater when the rays are more oblique.
Thus when one looks into an aquarium the back always
appears to be curved, and the fishes take queer shapes
as they swim about. If one poles a boat along in shallow

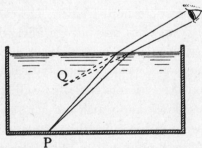

Fig. 43. When the view is more oblique, Q is nearer to the
surface, and does not lie immediately above P.

PLATE X

A. Ripples passing over a rectangular piece of glass laid on the floor of the ripple tank; showing the temporary change of alignment. (*p.* 69)

B. The dotted lines underneath the boat show how the bed of the river appears to the man in the boat if he looks down into it. (*p.* 71)

PLATE I

A. This picture of a soap film is due to the late Sir James Dewar: the scale alongside shows the thickness at different levels. One 'μ' is the ten thousandth part of a centimetre. (p. 144)

B. A coloured photograph showing a repetition of Newton's experiment in the laboratory. The light from the lantern in the bottom right hand corner passes through a horizontal slit which defines it and then through a prism which forms a spectrum on the lower of the two translucent screens held by the retort stand. A slit in this screen allows some of the green to pass on and strike a second prism. The green rays are bent to one side and strike the upper screen; no further resolution occurs, and the rays remain green. (pp. 85 and 88)

C. This coloured photograph is taken from above a rectangular tank containing water in which aesculin and eosin have been dissolved. The light from the lantern comes through the lens seen at the top of the picture and is deflected downwards upon the surface of the water by the prism, which also separates the colours. The spectrum of part of the light is seen upon a screen just above the surface of the water on the right. Where the spectrum falls on the surface itself, the light of the shorter waves is absorbed, and is replaced by light of somewhat longer waves. The aesculin fluoresces a blue and the eosin a yellowish green: the two fluorescing bands are to the left of the bright spectrum. There is a blue patch higher up in the centre which is a reflection in the glass wall of the tank and is to be disregarded. The longer waves pass through the liquid and make a yellowish red patch on the floor of the tank.

(p. 224)

D. This photograph is taken from the hand-coloured illustration in Young's *Natural Philosophy*. The vertical stripes of the lower part represent the interference colours of a soap film increasing gradually in thickness from left to right (in the actual experiment, top to bottom). The upper part of the figure shows what is observed when the lower is drawn out into a spectrum by a prism placed so that its edge is horizontal. For example, the bluish patches (meant to be quite blue) on the left are drawn out into spectra from which the red is missing. Adjoining the blues are yellows, which are drawn out into spectra containing all but the violet, and so on. The black patches group themselves into continuous curved bands. (p. 142)

water in which the boat barely floats, it seems always that the water ahead is so shallow that the boat is going aground. Yet as one comes up to it the water seems to deepen and the boat can still move on. A stick which is partly under water seems to be bent where it passes through the surface because every part of it which is immersed is apparently lifted up. The effect is illustrated in Plate Xʙ.

The refraction of the sun's rays by the atmosphere

Fig. 44. The observer looking towards the horizon receives rays from the sun below the horizon, because the rays are bent in going through the atmosphere.

has an effect on the apparent time of sunset. Since light travels more slowly in air than in space empty of material substances the sun's rays are bent out of their original course before they reach the earth. The change in direction is at maximum when the rays strike the surface of the atmosphere at their greatest obliquity, and this happens when the sun is on the horizon. Then, as Fig. 44 shows, rays from a point P on the sun's disc will reach the observer at O, although his horizon lies in the direction of OH: a direction which lies on the surface of still water at O. Thus the point P is still visible though it is below the horizon. The sun has set geometrically before it does so visually; the amount of the change of direction is such that the sun has set geometrically at

71

about the time when its lower edge just touches the horizon.

In the next chapter we shall consider the separation of white light into constituent colours during its refraction. We may anticipate so much as to observe that blues and greens are more refracted than yellow and reds. Consequently, the last rays which reach us from the setting sun are of the former kind unless, which is nearly always the case, other conditions interfere. Hence arises the so-called 'green ray' which sometimes flashes out for a few seconds just before sunrise or just after sunset, and is looked for when the air is very still and uniform.

Even when light passes from one gas to another it is bent if the densities of the gases are different: or from one part to another of the same gas if the density varies, as it may do on account of changes of temperature or of pressure. When a fire is lit in the open the objects quiver that are seen through the space above the flames because the rays of light are bent from side to side by the irregular mixture of hot and cold gases. The same effect is observed if one looks through the heated currents above a candle or a lamp. In hot countries the air near the ground is heated by its contact with the hot earth and the details of the distant landscape are never still.

Total Internal Reflection

There is a phenomenon known as 'total internal reflection' which is responsible for many curious effects. If we refer back to the experiment of Fig. 40 we may observe that the ray that just emerged from the tank after reflection at the bottom was previously inclined at a considerable angle to the surface of the water. We may ask ourselves what happens to a ray which strikes the surface from below at a smaller inclination. The experiment is easily made if the arrangement of the mirrors is altered. The mirror M_1 directs a pencil of light vertically downwards into the tank to a second mirror M_2 (Fig. 45). The inclination of the latter can be varied.

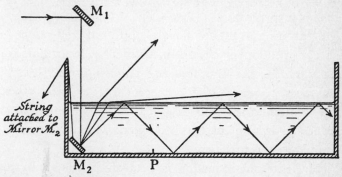

Fig. 45. Sectional diagram of a water tank arranged to show total internal reflection. A ray of light from the lantern is directed upon the mirror M1 and there reflected so as to strike the mirror M2. The latter can be tilted by means of a string attached to it. In one position it reflects a ray which emerges from the water easily: in another the ray just emerges and skims the surface: in a third it is internally reflected at the surface of the water. A mirror lies along the floor of the tank.

By tilting it gradually from the flat the reflected ray is made to strike the under surface of the water more and more obliquely. At a certain inclination the ray just succeeds in emerging as we have seen before: when this point is past the ray cannot get out at all, and is reflected down again. The reflection is complete: more perfect therefore than if the surface of the water were replaced by a silvered mirror: whence the name given to the phenomenon. If the tank is long enough in comparison with the depth of water the reflection at the top surface and the mirror at the bottom of the tank may be repeated several times. The effect is demonstrated in the photograph of Plate XIA.

A very simple method of observing total internal reflection is to put a spoon in a tumbler of water and look at the surface of the water from below, choosing a proper angle for doing so. Part of the spoon is reflected in the under surface of the water, and the brilliancy of the effect is surprising.

Great use is made of total internal reflection in the construction of optical instruments, binoculars for example. In the simplest case a glass prism is used, two faces of which are perpendicular to each other. Light enters at one face and leaves by the other after perfect reflection at a third face which is equally inclined to the first two.

Total internal reflection is beautifully shown by an experiment due to Tyndall and demonstrated by him at a Royal Institution lecture many years ago. The tank in the illustration (Plate XIB) is full of water which issues in a continuous stream from a jet near the bottom. The stream is unbroken all the way down to the cistern into which it falls almost noiselessly. A lens is inserted in the wall of the tank opposite to the jet, and a beam of light is thereby concentrated on the inside of the stream as it issues. The light is reflected many times in succession at the external surface of the stream, so that it looks as if the water carried the light down it. One may often observe the same effect when one pours water from a jug into a basin, though it is not so clearly shown as in the special experiment. A similar arrangement, with a curved glass

PLATE XI

A. This photograph of the actual experiment shows several total reflections at the surface of the water. It may be observed that the ray that finally issues is refracted in doing so. The mirror M_2 (Fig. 45) is rather more tilted than in the photograph of Plate VIII B. (*p.* 74)

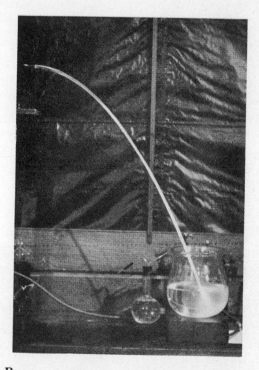

B. An experiment due to Tyndall illustrating total internal reflection. Light enters the jet of falling water at its point of issue from the tank and is carried down by the stream. The light is supplied by an electric arc outside the tank and focussed upon the jet by a lens in the tank wall. The arc and the lens do not appear in the photograph. (*p.* 74)

beam of light to illuminate an object under the microscope.

When the ground is strongly heated by the rays from
the sun the layers of air in contact with it may become
hotter than those at a little greater height. In such cases

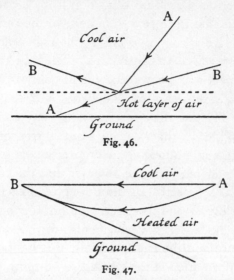

Fig. 46.

Fig. 47.

Figs. 46 and 47.   When the lower strata of the atmosphere are
hotter than those above them, rays of light may be refracted or
even internally reflected in the manner illustrated by these
figures.

there is an opportunity for total internal reflection of
light within the atmosphere which is a common cause
of mirage.

Suppose that for simplicity's sake we imagine the
condition represented in the diagram where a well
defined boundary separates the hot layer next the ground
from the cold layer above it.   A ray of light marked A in
Fig. 46 moves more nearly in a horizontal direction

after crossing the boundary, because the velocity of light in hot air is greater than in cold. The ray marked B meets the surface at so small a glancing angle that it is totally reflected as in a mirror. The separation between hot and cold strata is never as sharp as the diagram shows: there is a gradual transition from the hot to the cold. This makes no real difference to the result. The path of the ray is curved as Fig 47 shows instead of being sharply turned back as in Fig. 46. Thus the ray from a distant object may pass to the eye not only by the usual direct road, but also by the bent path as shown in Fig. 47. The eye may receive, as if they came out of the ground, rays that started from a tree or the sky behind it: and naturally the impression is given that there is water between the observer and the tree, water being always detected by its power of reflection. It is often possible to see this effect, on a hot day even in our own latitudes, when the pavements are raised to a high temperature and the eye, especially if it happens owing to the conformation of the ground to be more or less on a level with the pavement at a distance, may see there what appear to be reflections of the sky or of bright coloured dresses.

Certain curious phenomena which are found to occur in broadcasting are to be explained in a manner which bears a strong resemblance to this account of the mirage. In the upper regions of the atmosphere are layers which reflect the radio waves and turn them down again upon the earth. If it were not for this, long distance transmission would be practically impossible, particularly when short waves, say 50 metres, are used, because the waves would not follow the curvature of the earth with sufficient intensity. As we have already seen these waves are of exactly the same nature as those of light, so that the analogy is very close. The layers in question contain a number of electrified molecules and free electrons, the presence of which is due to radiation from the sun, particularly of wave-lengths shorter than those of light. These radiations spend their energies on partial disintegration of the molecules, stripping some of them of electrons which finally attach themselves to other molecules, so that both positive and negative charges and electrons are present in the atmosphere. There is a continuous recombination in progress, so that the state of the atmosphere is a balance between two processes. When the radiations are strong they bring to a higher pitch the electrification of the atmosphere through which they pass. Their energy is absorbed in the process, so that the air near the earth is never much affected. In higher regions the electrification is sufficient to have a noticeable effect on the propagation of the broadcasting waves. The reason for this is that in passing from the lower strata of the air into strata where there is electrification, the waves are refracted, or turned to one side in the same manner and in the same sense as a ray of light is bent on passing out of the water into the air in the experiment of Fig. 39. This effect is observed experimentally, and it can be accounted for by calculation based on the electromagnetic theory of light. For our present purpose it is enough to accept the fact.

Now, just as the ray of light of Fig. 45 is reflected

internally, when it strikes the surface from below at an angle which is sufficiently oblique, so, under similar conditions, the radio waves are reflected at the electrified layers of the upper atmosphere. If the electrification is intense enough, reflection will take place even when the rays strike the layer perpendicularly. But it happens frequently, especially at night time when there is a lesser degree of electrification, that reflection takes place only when the obliquity is sufficient. The reflected ray returns to earth and may be detected at places sufficiently far away, while at intermediate places no signal is received. In just the same way, in the experiment of Fig. 45 the reflected ray of light cannot strike the bottom of the tank at a point which is nearer the mirror M_2 than the point marked P on the diagram.

The passage from an unelectrified atmosphere to a stratum that contains separated electricities is not abrupt: nor is there any need that it should be so. The more gradual it is, the more does the path of the reflected ray assume a curved form during reflection as in Fig. 47.

There are at least two strata in the atmosphere which cause this reflection of radio waves: one of them at a height of rather more than a hundred kilometres, between sixty and seventy miles. This has long been known as the Kennelly-Heaviside layer. There is another of very variable height, several times as far away from the earth's surface: this was discovered in 1927 by Professor Appleton. Signals sent from East London College are received at King's College in the Strand like sound echoes from a ceiling: and more than one echo is received for each signal. Thus the record of Fig. 48 indicates the receipt of an interesting set of echoes. The wavy line is a time scale, 1,115 complete waves go to one second. The prominence marked G marks the moment when the signal was received by way of the ground, practically at the moment of its emission. At E, is the mark of the arrival of the first echo from the lowest layer. At F, the signal comes back again from the higher layer, at S is a small echo coming from a distance so great that the cause of it is as yet unknown.

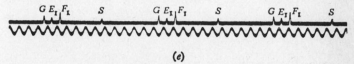

(e)

Fig. 48. A record showing the reflection of radio waves in various atmospheric layers. (E. V. Appleton.)

It is interesting to observe that sound also finds layers in the upper atmosphere at which it may be reflected if it strikes them with sufficient obliquity. These layers are probably connected in some way with the layers we have been discussing. The absorption of the sun's radiation to which the electrification is due must generate heat, and it has recently been calculated that there must be layers in the upper atmosphere where the temperature is very high. In heated air sound travels more quickly than the normal, and thus the bending of the sound rays takes place in a manner quite analogous to the light effects which we have been considering. It is due to this effect that echoes of intense sounds can be heard, not only close to the source, but also at great distances, while nothing is heard at regions in between.

79

A very interesting example of the application of the laws of reflection and refraction is to be found in the gem-cutter's treatment of precious stones: and particularly of the diamond. It is always surprising to read

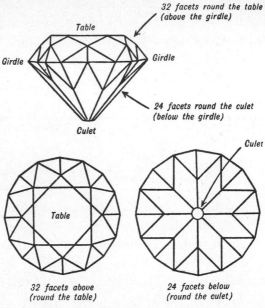

Fig. 49. The upper figure shows a section of the diamond cut as a brilliant: the lower figures show the arrangement of the facets above and below the girdle.

that something like half the whole mass of a diamond may be cut away before the stone is supposed to have acquired its full virtue as a gem. The explanation is that the diamond must be shaped to one or other of certain standard designs, which have been found to give the best effects. The best of all is the 'brilliant,' said to have been invented by Cardinal Mazarin. It is shown in elevation, and in plan in Fig. 49. The two lower drawings show the disposition of facets above and below the girdle.

When the diamond is cut to this form it allows no ray to go through it from front to back. If it is held against the light with the culet towards the eye, and the table away from the eye, it looks black. All rays falling on

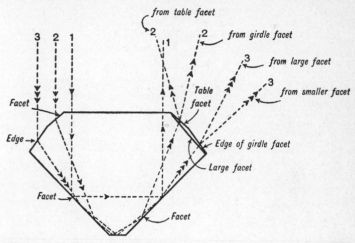

Fig. 50. The figure shows a few of the various paths by which a ray of light entering the brilliant from the front is refracted and 'totally internally' reflected until it leaves again through the front, never succeeding in getting through the diamond.

the front of the diamond are returned and emerge again on the front side. They will not in general, return in exactly the same direction: each ray will usually emerge at some other facet than that by which it entered. In Fig. 50 are drawn some of the paths by which light may enter and leave. In this way the diamond acquires the power of sparkling which is so much esteemed. Wherever it may be and however it may be held with respect to the eye, it is almost certain that the eye will receive from the gem some ray which has originated in one of the sources of illumination in the room or from the light of the sky. It may be said to be continually reflecting light from unexpected sources. It cannot of course give more than it receives, but its reflections are so numerous and bright, and vary so frequently that they

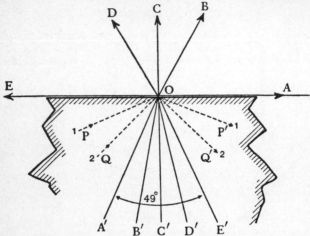

Fig. 51. The refractive index of diamond is very large. A ray A′ O A just succeeds in emerging. Rays such as Q O Q′ are reflected internally. The paths may be followed in either direction.

give great pleasure to the eye. These are increased by the resolution of the white light into colours, which as we shall see presently always accompanies an act of refraction.

The peculiar property of the material of the diamond, which is simply a crystallised form of carbon, is the very large refraction which it imposes on light that enters it. This is illustrated in Fig. 51. The rays A, B, C, D, E, are bent on entering and proceed in the directions A′ B′ C′ D′ E′. Light moves much slower in diamond than

PLATE XII

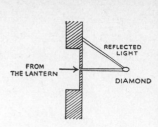

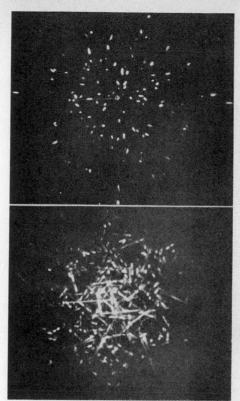

A. Reflections from a single diamond. The light is admitted into a room through a small opening in the wall, as shown in the accompanying drawing. The hole can also be seen in the centre of the photograph. The fine pencil of light is just visible up to the point where it strikes the diamond and is there divided into a great number of reflected beams each making a spot on the wall. (*p.* 83)

B. The same arrangement as the preceding but a zircon is substituted for the diamond. (*p.* 84)

C. Newton's Experiment, from a drawing in Guillemin's *Forces of Nature*. The ray of sunlight is resolved into a spectrum by the first prism: a portion of the spectrum is allowed to pass through a slit in the screen and fall upon a second prism, but no further resolution takes place. (*pp.* 85 *and* 88)

in air: the ratio of the velocities averages about 2.5, varying with the wave-length. For this reason the total internal reflection also has remarkable characteristics. Rays following the line A'O, B'O . . . E'O will emerge on the lines OA, OB . . . But the first and last will only just emerge and after doing so will skim the surface. Rays starting for O from the points 1, 2, along the lines PO, QO, will not emerge at all, and will be internally reflected along the lines OP', OQ'. The angle A'OE' is only 49°. If now we consider the section of the diamond as shown in Fig. 50 we see how this large possibility of internal reflection is put to advantage. A ray entering the crystal directly through the table and at right angles to it is totally reflected when it meets from within one of the facets below the girdle: it strikes across and is again reflected in the same way, so that it emerges from the table in a direction which is simply the reverse of that by which it entered. If it enters by one of the facets above the girdle, being still parallel to the axis of the stone, it emerges by some other of the upper facets: and even if the original ray is inclined to the axis, it may still emerge at the front. One or two possible paths are shown in the diagram: they may represent movement of the light in either sense along each path.

A lecture room experiment shows these effects very beautifully. A fine pencil of rays is allowed to enter the room from an arc light outside, and the diamond is held a few feet away from the point of entry, the table being square to the pencil. The whole wall of the darkened room is then starred with hundreds of reflections from the diamond, which, whenever the diamond is moved, follow paths that interlace each other in intricate and dazzling patterns (Plate XIIA).

Other stones like the sphene or the zircon show effects as fine: but they are not so valuable as gems because they are so much softer than the diamond. Reflections from zircon are shown in Plate XIIB.

CHAPTER III

COLOUR

The Colour Spectrum

THERE is a quality of light which we call colour. We ask ourselves the question – on what feature of the light mechanism does colour depend ?

If light be considered as a train of waves in a medium which we name as the ether, an answer to the question can be put into words at once. Colour depends upon the wave-length of light, that is to say, on the distance between the crest of any wave and its successor. The proof of this simple statement is better deferred for the moment, but it is convenient and helpful to bear the fact in mind.

The light from any source can generally be analysed into a series of components which severally give the sensation of colour. The components cannot be sharply separated but melt into one another by smooth gradation. The simplest method of analysis depends on the use of a glass prism. This was the way by which Newton approached the long series of experiments which laid the foundation of physical optics and formed one of his greatest contributions to science. His arrangement is shown in Plate XIIc and IB. A pencil of sunlight enters a dark room through a hole in a shutter, and falls upon a glass prism as the figure shows. On emergence the

analysis is complete: the light is drawn out into a
coloured band known as the spectrum. The red end of
the spectrum is formed by the rays that are least bent
on going through the prism, the violet by the rays that

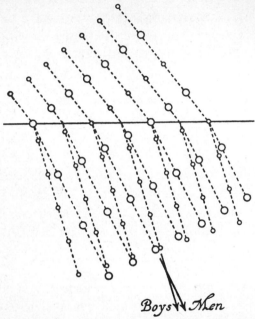

Boys *Men*

Fig. 52. In the upper part of the diagram alternate rows of men, larger circles,
and boys, smaller circles, are marching over smooth ground and keeping their
alignments and distances. The lower part is rough ground, and the rows of
boys are swung round more than the rows of men. It is supposed for the
purpose of the analogy that each row tries to keep its own alignment: and
that the rows do not get in each other's way. The distances between the
rows do *not* represent wave lengths.

are bent the most. Other colours are ranged between
the two limits without any clear lines of demarcation,
though a natural definition of colour finds in the spectrum band, red, orange, yellow, green, and various
shades of blue and violet. A colour photograph of the
spectrum is shown in Plate XIVD.

The red waves are found – we are again anticipating – to be the longest of those that we see in the spectrum: at the other end of the spectrum are the shortest. We have already used the analogy of a line of men on the march who come to difficult ground which cuts their front obliquely. Just as the line tends to swing round and become more nearly parallel to the line which separates the easy ground from the difficult, so the advancing waves alter their direction, and in the same sense. We may now extend the analogy. If the marching ranks are formed of small boys and not of men, the deflection will be greater still because their short legs will be more impeded by the roughness of the ground on which they enter. If there are both men and boys, as the illustration of Fig. 52 shows, the men will become separated from the boys: the latter will swing their ranks round more than the men and will not only lag behind but will actually march away in a different direction. In the same way the waves that are short are separated by the prism from those that are long: and the analogy may serve as a reminder that the former are more deflected than the latter.

Waves of all lengths or all colours travel at the same rate in free space. If it were not so, a star, disappearing behind some other heavenly body, for example the moon, would be coloured. If the blue rays travelled the slowest the disappearing star would be blue: and correspondingly it would appear red when it emerged again. In a transparent medium light travels more slowly than in space, and in general the short or blue wave more slowly than the red.

The figures show an extension of Newton's experiment. A small portion of the spectrum is allowed to pass through a hole in the screen and to fall upon a second prism. It then appears that the separation by the first prism has been complete: the selected pencil is not opened out into a spectrum like the original pencil and no new colours appear. There is indeed a slight enlargement because the two slits through which the light has passed must have a certain width and this leads to some overlapping. The second slit therefore lets through a selection of wave-lengths or colours which the second prism opens out somewhat. The narrower the slits and the more selective they become, the less is this effect. On the contrary, if the first slit is opened wide, the patches on the screen due to the several colours so overlap that in the centre all the colours combine to form white, as is shown in Plate XIVA.

These experiments show that refraction by the prism, and indeed by any means which takes advantage of the variation of speed with wave-length effects an analysis which is immediately complete. To the eye it appears as a separation into colours: it will presently be shown that it can be better defined as a separation into waves of different lengths.

The Quality of Light

Now comes a very important point. When the prism has effected its analysis, it is found to be impossible to make any further separation which the eye can detect. We have come to the end of the visible qualities of light. Light has velocity, which is the same for all wave-lengths in free space, and varies otherwise with the wave-length and the nature of the medium through which the light is passing, whence refraction and spectrum analysis. It has intensity, obviously: and wave-length. This is all, so far as vision is concerned. There is one other characteristic known as the degree of polarisation, which depends in a very simple manner upon the direction in which the waves carry out their individual motions. Waves on the sea rise and fall: but in the case of light there is no such unique direction, the movement may be from side to side as well as up and down, or in any other direction intermediate between the two. This effect will come up for consideration in its proper place later on: it escapes the eye and is only mentioned now so that the list of the qualities of light may be complete.

The nature of a ray of light is therefore specified completely, so far as the eye is concerned, when its intensity and its wave-length are defined If the ray is complex, consisting of a mixture of rays of differing wave-lengths, it is further necessary to state the intensity of each component: but that is all. There is indeed an infinite additional complexity of our colour sensations which is due, not to variations in the quality of light itself, but to variations in the reactions of eye and brain. The former must be distinguished from the latter.

The Range of Wave-lengths

It will be observed that the method of picturing light to ourselves as a form of wave motion has so far, at least, been of excellent service. The essential qualities of

89

visible light are just those which a wave motion conveniently represents. This being the case we naturally ask ourselves whether our experiences of the behaviour of other waves, water waves for example, suggest any effects to which we should expect to find parallels in the case of light.

Now, a very obvious characteristic of waves upon the sea is the wide variation that exists in wave-length, that is to say in the distance between the crests of successive waves. At one extreme is the long ocean swell, at the other the tiny ripple that is raised by a light puff of wind. When we consider light from this point of view we are at once struck by a fact of singular interest. The only waves that are visible are those of which the wave-length is confined within a very narrow range.

The wave-length of red light is rather less than the ten thousandth of a centimetre, that of the short waves at the other end of the spectrum is not quite half so much. All the other visible wave-lengths fall in between these two extremes.

Are no other wave-lengths possible therefore? Is there something in light which has so far escaped us, so that our wave theory fails because it does not suggest the limitations to which vision is subject?

Experiment shows that the wave theory has not failed us, and that the limitation is to be found in our powers of vision, not in what could be seen were our eyes constituted differently. We have experiences now of an enormous range of wave-lengths, from those which are used in broadcasting, and are measured in hundreds of metres, to those which are emitted by certain radioactive substances and are tens of thousands of times shorter than anything that we can see. The range over which our eyes are effective is only a minute fraction of the whole, on whatever scale we make out our estimate.

For the time we keep ourselves to this narrow range, naturally of immense importance to us since all the phenomena of vision fall within it. All matters of colour depend upon the way in which the waves of this region are produced, are affected by reflection from bodies at their surfaces, or by transmission through them, and finally are received and interpreted by eye and brain.

The Action of a Pigment

We set up an arrangement by which the light from an arc lantern issues from a slit and falls upon a lens which makes an image of the slit upon a screen. We place a prism in front of the slit and the narrow white image is drawn out into the coloured spectrum as in Plate XIVD. The spectrum may be looked upon as a series of over-lapping images of the slit due to the various wave-lengths into which the prism resolves the incident light. We place a piece of red glass before the slit: this wipes out all the colours in the spectrum except the red (Plate XIVE). We observe that there is no conversion of one colour into another: the only action is destructive. A piece of red glass does not acquire its characteristic property by turning other colours into red: it destroys all but the red. This is indeed the essential feature of all coloration: colour is due to a sifting and to a removal of all colours except residues: which latter make the colour of the object that has been responsible for the sifting.

If we look carefully at the red image that is left upon the screen when the red glass is in use we see that while the top and bottom of the image are sharp, the sides are not. The former are the images of the top and bottom of the slit, and light of every wave-length puts them in line. But the vagueness of the sides shows that it is not light of exactly one wave-length which makes the image, but light drawn from a narrow range of wave-lengths about the red. Thus there is a little overlapping.

If we use a piece of yellow glass the overlapping becomes very marked (Plate XIVF). In fact the spectrum seems, when we first look at it, to have been hardly affected, but a closer inspection shows that the extreme blue end has gone. It is surprising that the yellow glass should allow such a complex set of wave-lengths to pass. We are inclined to say that the colour of the yellow is pure. Since we find by experiment that the light transmitted by the yellow glass contains a great variety of wave-lengths each of which would separately affect the eye in a different way, we must conclude that the prism and the eye do not give us the same definition of 'purity.' This is an extraordinarily interesting feature of the process of vision. Before we consider this in detail however, let us proceed a little further with the phenomenon of coloration.

Coloured liquids, like coloured glass, produce colour by the destruction of colour. This process is also the cause of the coloration of solids. When we lay a wash of water-colour upon a piece of white paper we do not produce light of new quality, but destroy some that already existed. The white paper on which we paint reflects all colours that fall upon it. We lay down a sheet of a transparent liquid, through which light passes twice before it reaches our eyes, once on the way to the white paper below, and again after reflection there. If this liquid absorbs all the wave-lengths except the red, then red alone is returned to the eye: we have laid down a wash of red. If the liquid absorbs the violet only, then the paper reflects to us a yellow: if the liquid absorbs red only, the resulting colour is a greenish blue and so on. When wash after wash of different colours is laid upon the paper the number of destructive agents is increased: and of course in unskilful hands the residue of colour that reaches the eye may be dull and dirty.

A different plan is followed in oil painting. The pigment contains 'body,' that is to say a solid substance which reflects and scatters the incident light, and does the duty of the white paper in water-colour painting. Thus the light does not reach the canvas: and one layer of paint may be thick enough to hide completely a layer on which it is laid. The same effect is produced in water-colours by mixing the paint with Chinese white.

The fact that a pigment produces colour by destruction of colour is of course in direct contradiction of the idea that one colour can be converted into another as we are apt to suppose. Here again, we see that the wave theory informs us rightly. We know that a set of waves cannot change directly into a set of waves of different wave-length. An ocean swell does not become a set of ripples in passing through an opening or on being reflected from a wall. Red light is not to be expected therefore to become blue or vice versâ when it passes through a coloured transparency, or is reflected from an object. The source of light is the source of all the colours in the light. We must suppose that in some way the white light from the sun contains the whole range of spectrum colours before it is analysed by the prism.

If we analyse in the same way the light from any other source we find in general, that the spectrum colours are not generally the same. The spectrum of the yellow flame of a paraffin lamp, for example, contains none of the short wave-lengths. Even the spectrum of the sun varies from time to time. A piece of blue cloth acquires the colour by which it is named because in full daylight its dye absorbs most of the light that falls upon it and returns only deep blue to the eye. In the light of the paraffin lamp it looks black because the light does not contain the only colour which it can reflect: it reflects nothing therefore.

If we take a bunch of primroses of nominally 'pure yellow' and cause the colours of the spectrum to fall successively upon it, the colour of the bunch changes with its position. In the red the flowers look red, in the yellow they appear in their natural colour, in the green they look green, but in the deep blue they look black. This last is the only 'wave-length' which they do not reflect. In the same way the colour of any object, as it appears to us, depends not only upon its own pigment-ation, but also upon the light which makes it visible. The sunlight as it streams into a room may strike first

94

a white wall or a coloured wall or carpet, and the whole colour scheme of the room is affected thereby.

What then is 'white' from which all our colours seem to be derived by analysis? We are apt to say, of course, that it is the ordinary light of day. But, as we have seen, the latter varies in quality: the photographer knows that well. As the sun sinks towards its setting the light becomes relatively richer in orange and red. On the top of a high mountain it contains more blue than on the surface of the earth. White daylight is not therefore easy to define. There is a certain average composition of wave-lengths which we call 'white': and the definition is sufficient for ordinary use. If greater precision is required the relative strengths of the components should be specified, either directly, or indirectly, in terms of some light standards which can themselves be correctly and fully described. There is no such thing as a light which is absolutely white: whiteness is a quality of our own definition. We can with better cause speak of the surface of a piece of paper or other body being white, because the natural meaning of such a term would be that the surface reflects, or scatters completely light of every quality. It is a passive quality, as compared with the active quality of light. A white surface looks red in red light, blue in blue light, and so on. But even then the name is earned by the power of reflecting equally the visible rays within the narrow range that is perceived by the eye: if we went outside that range it might be necessary to revise our terms of description. A transparent and colourless liquid like benzene allows the visible rays to pass. But if our range of vision included the lengths just shorter than those of violet, we should call benzene a coloured liquid, because it absorbs these ultra-violet rays.

The Reactions of the Eye to Colour

So much for the part that the quality of light plays in producing the sensation of colour. We must now consider the reaction of the eye to that which it receives.

It is convenient to begin with an experiment. We take two arc lanterns and arrange them so that, with the help of circular apertures and lenses, they cast two bright white discs upon the screen: we can move one of the lanterns or lenses so that the discs overlap. If we place a piece of blue glass in front of one of the lanterns and a yellow glass in front of the other, the over-lapping portion receives blue light from one lantern and yellow from the other. To the eye, this portion is white. Now we know that yellow and blue paints when mixed together make a green: and there is an apparent contradiction. But this is soon resolved. If we place both blue and yellow glasses in front of one of the lanterns, the disc which that lantern throws is actually green. This is what we should expect, because the yellow glass as we have seen cuts out the blue end of the spectrum, and we may easily show that the blue glass cuts out the red. If a ray of light, originally white, is made to go through both glasses only the middle of the spectrum is left, which is preponderatingly green. But when we throw the blue and yellow discs upon the screen and find the overlap to be white, we are not causing successive absorptions to be made. We are doing something quite different: we are causing blue light and yellow light to be received in the eye at the same time. The combination in the overlap contains all the colours of the spectrum, and though the central colours may be in excess yet the eye accepts the whole as a reasonable white.

If we make the same experiment with red and green glasses we obtain the same sort of result. The overlap is a yellow: when the two glasses are placed in front of the same lantern they intercept all the light and the screen is dark. Examination with the aid of the prism shows that the red glass cuts out all but the red, and the green glass cuts out the red, and part of the blue. Thus no light can get through the two together while the overlap yields every colour but blue: and as we have seen already the eye then sees a yellow (Plate XIVᴮ).

In such experiments we come across the extraordinary fact that a colour which seems pure to the eye may be a very complex compound of many qualities of light, each of which could by itself produce its own colour. At a certain point in the spectrum is a yellow which is due to light of a very restricted range of wave-lengths: while the yellow that can pass the yellow glass contains nearly every visible wave-length. Further enquiry shows that there is no limit to the number of ways of composing a yellow which present one and the same appearance to the eye. This is very remarkable because the behaviour of the ear, in its own sphere, is so curiously different. In the world of sound intelligence is conveyed by wave motions in a manner analogous to that which we have, at least temporarily, assumed as characteristic of the universe of light. But in the former case the carrying media are certainly material, the air or other gases, liquids, or solids. In the case of sound as in that of light the length of the wave affects the sensation. The shorter the wave-length, the higher the pitch of the note and vice versâ. For the lowest note of the piano the wave-length is many feet: for the highest it is only one or two inches. So far the analogy between light and sound is complete: but it breaks down when combination effects are compared. We have seen that when two beams of light of different wave-lengths are together thrown into the eye a sensation of pure colour is perceived: the eye is incapable of recognising a mixture, and of analysing its components. But in the case of sound the ear can always recognise as such a mixture of different frequencies: a chord is analysed, and it may or may not give pleasure according to its composition. This is an essential contribution to music: how great it is we may realise if we consider the appalling consequences that would follow the replacement of every chord by some average note to be recognised as a 'pure' tone.

Many have attempted to construct an instrument by which the appeal to our senses is to be made through the play of colour upon a screen: each key is to throw in light of a particular colour. The attempts have always failed badly in that nothing so powerful as music has been achieved. It may well be that the failure is due to the incapacity of the eye to resolve a 'chord' of colour. There is far less analogy between the eye and ear than some have thought who have proposed to make 'colour organs.' The simultaneous projection of several colours upon different parts of a screen might be considered to be the analogue of the projection of several sounds into the

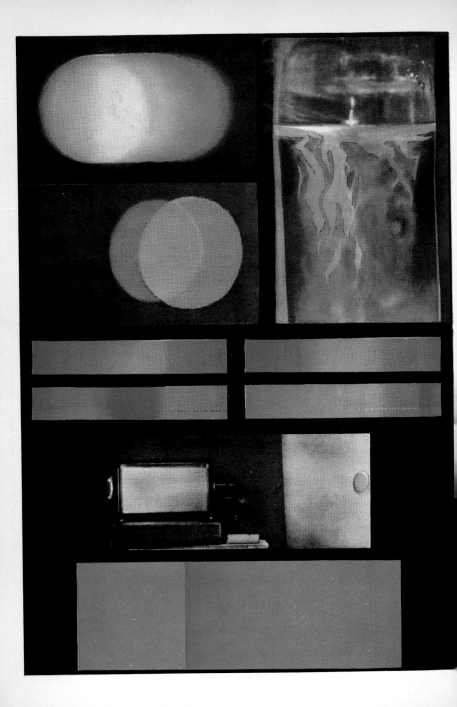

PLATE XIV

A. The spectrum here shown differs from that of XIIc. or IB., in that the slit has been replaced by a circular opening. The overlapping images are now circular, and in the centre of the picture the colour is nearly a white because nearly all the images overlap there. (p. 88)

C. Light from above falls on the jar containing water into which various fluorescent substances have been dropped in powder form. They are falling slowly in the water and dissolving as they do so. (p. 224)

B. The overlapping discs are due to separate lanterns. The rays from one lantern have passed through red glass, from the other through green glass. The red and green patches form a yellow where they overlap. A coloured photograph of the experiment. (p. 97)

D. The spectrum photographed in colour. The rays of the lantern have passed through a narrow slit : and the picture is really a series of images of the slit due to light of different colours or wave-lengths. (p. 86)

E. A piece of red glass placed in the path of the white light cuts off nearly all the colours except those near the red end of the spectrum so that the latter is greatly reduced in extent. (p. 91)

F. A piece of yellow glass cuts off the violet only. (p. 92)

G. A solution of chlorophyll absorbs certain portions of the spectrum, particularly a portion of the extreme red. A coloured photograph of the altered spectrum. (p. 118)

H. Light from the lantern is robbed of part of its blue in going through the vessel filled with liquid containing fine particles in suspension. The remainder forms a red disc upon the screen, like the setting sun. (p. 150)

J. The purple patch in the centre does not appear to the eye to be uniform in colour. It looks bluish purple beside the red patch, and reddish purple beside the blue. (p. 102)

PLATE XIII

A. The old inscription on the base runs:—THE FIRST REFLECTING TELLESCOPE INVENTED BI SR ISAAC NEWTON AND MADE WITH HIS OWN HANDS IN THE YEAR 1671. *By permission of the Officers of the Royal Society.* Height about 18in. (*p*.107)

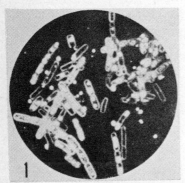
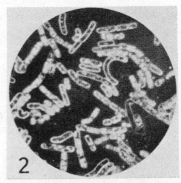

B. Micro-photographs of bacteria (B Megatherium x 2000) by Mr. J. E. Barnard, F.R.S. (1) taken in visible light under the best attainable condition; (2) taken in ultra-violet light (2743 A).
Objects which appear as round white discs in (1) are resolved into greater detail in (2).
(*p.* 109)

air at the same time; but analogies are proverbially unsafe as bases for argument.

It is generally held that the ear mechanism comprises a set of receivers each of which responds only to sounds lying within a narrow range of frequencies. It may be likened to a room full of sharply tuned wireless sets. The eye cannot be compared to anything so diverse and selective: its receivers must be fewer and less special. Naturally, a very large amount of research has been spent in the attempt to understand the receiving mechanism. It is not surprising that the solution of a problem so intricate is not yet fully in hand. Certain main conclusions have been reached however, and there is a general agreement that – to use for descriptive purposes the analogy with the wireless – there are three receivers, each widely responsive, like a radio-set which cannot be tuned sharply. Two respond best to the ends of the visible spectrum, and one to the wave-lengths in the middle: each is responsive to some extent to the greater part of the spectrum. Our sensations of colour depend on the relative responses of the three to the light which enters the eye. If any one of the three, say that which is most responsive to red, is missing or only partly efficient, the eye is more or less insensitive to the presence of red: there is a difficulty in distinguishing red flowers from green leaves. Quite a number of people are colour blind because of such a defect: the red receiver being the one that is most usually at fault. The owner of the eye may be totally unaware of its defect. John Dalton, the famous pioneer chemist did not know that he was colour blind until the fact was discovered by

Thomas Young when Dalton was forty years old. Theories of the exact ranges of these receivers are mainly based on comparisons between the perceptions of the normal and the colour blind eye.

We can now see how it is possible to devise various combinations of wave-lengths which will seem alike to the eye. A particular colour sensation is due to the stimulations of the three receivers in proper proportions. Since every wave-length can stimulate at least two and often all three, but in different proportions, a required sensation can, within certain obvious limits, be obtained by the use of any three wave-lengths provided their relative intensities are properly adjusted.

Complementary Colours

If we suppose that these receiving organs can be tired by use and become less efficient, we can readily find an explanation for the frequent appearance of complementary colours, so called. If we look steadily at some brightly coloured object for a few seconds and then look away at an illuminated surface, preferably white, we see a patch of a different colour which floats before our eyes and moves as we turn them. The explanation is that the receivers are not equally fatigued. If we have been looking at red, the red receiver is more fatigued than the others, so that when white light is thrown into the eye the other two receivers are more fully stimulated and a bluish green appears.

A striking example of the effect can be obtained by using the whole spectrum, as thrown upon the white screen by the arc light. We gaze steadily at a fixed point in the spectrum, which we mark in some way, and after about a quarter of a minute we put the arc out and light up the room. Something like a reverse spectrum then appears, blue and green where the red was before, and red in place of the blue: in the centre purple replaces some of the brighter colours there.

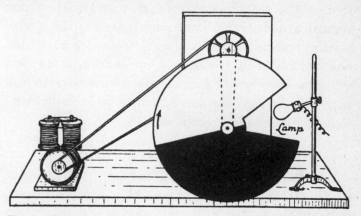

Fig. 53. The disc is rotated in the direction which is indicated by the arrow. The lamp, which is red, is visible at intervals through the open sector. It appears green, and not red. The disc must be well illuminated.

One would expect the complementary colours observed in these ways to be much feebler than the original, but there is a very curious experiment which shows that the contrary may be true. We prepare a circular cardboard disc of about eighteen inches diameter, cut out of it a sector and divide the remainder into black and white halves as in Fig. 53. We mount the disc so that it can be turned round its axis at the rate of two or three times a second. We put a red lamp at L as the figure shows: we light up the front of the disc strongly and make it revolve. As it turns we see the red-looking filament for a short time, then the white half of the disc, then the black, then the filament again and so on. When the white part of the disc hides the lamp we must, as we know, see a green reaction. The interesting fact is that this green is so much stronger than the red that when the disc is in motion we do not see the latter at all. The reaction produces more effect than the original action. It is most curious to see the green filament replace the red. If we turn the disc the other way, the colour of the lamp is unchanged, it remains red; for in this case the black sector covers the lamp just after we have seen the latter, and there is no light to excite the secondary reactions.

Colour Illusions

Effects of this kind are due to peculiar features of our eyes, over which we have no control. Other effects are no doubt due in part to the adoption of false standards: we have already seen instances of this, and now find that in matters of colour it may also be operative. If for example, we lay side by side three patches of colour, red, purple and blue, in the order given, we find that there is difficulty in persuading ourselves that the purple is uniform (Plate XIVj). It seems reddish where it touches the blue, and bluish where it touches the red. We may suppose that we look at the red for a moment, so that we tire our red receiving organs, and then when our eyes look at the purple its red is not so fully seen. We may suppose also that near the red we form a false standard of what we mean by purple, making it too red because we are momentarily accustomed to an excess of red. The two explanations are not one and the same, but it may be difficult to decide between them.

The effect is, of course, made use of freely in the various modes of painting and of decoration in which colour is employed. One 'brings out' a certain colour, or alters its apparent hue by putting the appropriate colour beside it.

If we hang a picture on the wall, its appearance may be affected by all the various influences which we have been considering. There is in the first place the quality of the light that enters the room or that we provide purposely: the light is modified on reflection from the various objects in the room before it reaches the picture, and finally our perceptions are modified by the surroundings and by the coloration of the objects on which our eyes have rested just before we looked at the picture, or which we may look at from time to time. Presumably the ideal way to present a picture is to give to it illumination of the same intensity and quality as that under which it was painted, and to surround it as the artist intended it to be surrounded. A painting made out of doors in bright daylight does not then present the same appearance to the eye as it does at night when lit by ordinary sources of artificial illumination, and looked at by eyes that have changed their standard when the daylight failed. If the light from a paraffin lamp falls upon a piece of white paper alongside which is a piece of the same paper illuminated by daylight – the experiment is not difficult to arrange in the laboratory – the former appears orange brown as compared with the latter. Yet at night the former may be our standard of white; and

objects of other colours show, of course, similar variations. In these days of bright and plentiful illumination
the difference between day and night is not so great,
but even the brightest and whitest 'half-watt' electric
light does not correspond to daylight. It is necessary to
reduce very considerably the intensity of the long wave-
lengths of the artificial light by the use of a blue globe if
a near approach to daylight is to be attained. The
electric light contains the blue rays, but in insufficient
quantity. The use of daylight lamps has been much extended of late for various reasons; shops require them if
they must display goods where only artificial light is
available: sometimes the artist or the decorator is glad
of their help. It is startling to see the alteration of the
relative values of colours when the nature of the illumination is concerned. Two pieces of cloth may look green
in daylight: by artificial light one is green and one
brown, and so on.

The Colour Effects of Lenses

A lens is unable, unless special and quite elaborate
precautions are taken, to bring to a focus all the light
from a bright source, because whenever white light is
bent out of its course the blue is bent more than the red.
Fig. 54 shows how the rays will go: the blue rays come
to a point nearer to the lens than the red rays do. If
we put a piece of white paper at A, it has a red fringe,
if we move it to B, the fringe is blue. Nowhere are all
the colours brought to the same point.

The eye shows this effect. It is often possible on looking at the bright sky through an opening, a window for

example, to see a red or blue edging to the rectangle of
the window, the particular colour depending on the circumstances which influence the focusing of the eye.
This inability to focus all wave-lengths at the same time
troubles us very little. In the case of optical instruments when magnification is required a corresponding
inability would be fatal: fortunately it is possible to
design 'achromatic' lenses – as we shall see in a moment
– so that the difficulty is got over.

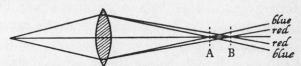

Fig. 54.   A lens brings the blue rays to a focus at a point A nearer
to the lens than the focus of the red rays at B.

The lack of achromatism in the eye has some curious
results. Since red rays are less bent than blue, the lens
system of the eye must be more compressed if it is to be
adapted to the vision of a red object. Now, the extent
of the strain that we have to put upon our eye muscles
is a partial indication of the nearness of an object: the
greater the strain the nearer we think it to be. We
are apt therefore to misjudge distances, estimating the
distance of red objects as less than that of blue, other
things being equal. This is probably the reason why a
red room looks smaller than a blue room. Perhaps we
associate blue with distance, from our experiences out of
doors: but the former reason seems to be the stronger.
The red letters in a brightly coloured poster seem to
stand out in front of the blue. Also, if there are objects
blue and red of the same size and at the same distance

from us, we are apt to think that the blue are the larger because we suppose them to be further away than the red.

A very interesting illustration of this curious illusion is to be found in the French tricouleur. The three vertical bands, red, white and blue, are not of equal width. Originally the widths were to be equal, but it was found that the blue looked larger than the red. A Commission of Enquiry examined the question and recommended that the widths of blue, white and red, should be in the proportion 30, 33 and 37: these figures being chosen as the result of experiment. With this arrangement the bands seem to the eye to be of equal value. It may be supposed that the eye would naturally imagine the blue to be further away than the red, and this being the case, the fact that the angles subtended by blue and red are actually equal, would lead to the further interpretation that the blue is larger than the red. It must be said however that modern writers consider the full explanation to be more complicated. (Hartridge, *Journal of Physiology*, 52, 222, 1918).

In a blue light vision is clear at closer distances than in a red light. The shorter wave-lengths are brought to a focus on the retina when the longer converge to a point behind it, even when all the converging power of the eye is brought to bear. This accounts, at least in part, for the fact that the details of one's immediate surroundings are more distinctly seen in a blue light than in a red.

The separation of colours that accompanies every attempt to bend a ray of white light becomes a serious matter when optical instruments are used to reinforce the powers of the eye, because the magnification is

the eye causes, and is accompanied by a greater separation of colours. In the view given by a poor pair of
binoculars the brightly illuminated parts are surrounded
by troublesome colour fringes. In the high magnifica-
tions of more powerful instruments the effect would be
intolerable if it were permitted.

It is curious that Newton believed the difficulty to be
insuperable: for which reason he abandoned the use of

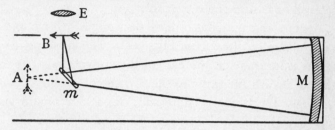

Fig. 55. A diagram showing the arrangement of Newton's telescope.

the lens as the object glass of his telescope and employed
a spherical reflector instead. The mirror could form an
image to be examined at close quarters by an eyepiece,
just as a lens could: and there would be no separations
of colour. In the diagram of Fig. 55, M is the large concave mirror which would form an image at A were it
not that a small plane mirror turns aside the rays from
M so that an image is formed at B. There the eyepiece
takes charge. If the image had been at A, the head of
the observer would have been in the road. A picture
of this telescope is shown in Plate XIIIA.

There is, however, a way of avoiding the coloration
which was first put into practice by John Dollond, who
in 1758 presented to the Royal Society the first achromatic telescope. Its construction depends on the fact

that the separation of colour which accompanies bending is not proportional to it for different qualities of glass. Two lenses can be constructed, one of crown glass, the other of the heavier flint glass, which will separate the spectrum colours equally and yet refract the ray as a whole through different angles. The passage of a beam of light through a convex lens of crown glass might be of the character shown in Fig. 56a, the blue rays being focused at B, and the red at R.

Again a concave lens of flint glass might behave to the same beam as shown in Fig. 56b. The bending as a whole is less than in the case of the crown glass, but the separation a is the same in the two cases.

If now the two are combined, the colour separations will be compensated but not the bendings as a whole. The converging power of the crown lens is greater than the diverging power of the flint lens. The two together will act as in the Fig. 56c.

In this way a beam of rays is brought to a point without the production of colour: the combination is achromatic. Yet this statement must be qualified, it would be better to say nearly achromatic. Any two wavelengths such as have been indicated by B, a point in the blue, and R, a point in the red, can be brought together again at the same focus in the way described. But the spectrum of wave-lengths is not spread out in the same way by the two lenses: the B and the R may be brought exactly together, other points in the spectrum are only made to coincide nearly. The evil is greatly corrected, but is not quite removed.

In the case of the microscope a further step to clear

vision is obtained by restricting the wave-lengths used to a narrow range. Of course this affects colour: but colour may be less desired than sharp outline. Some

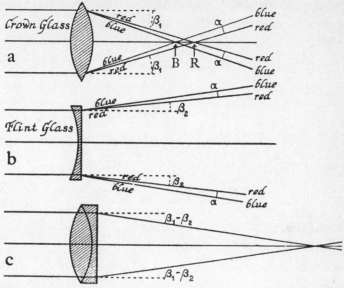

Fig. 56. The top figure shows a lens of crown glass. Its converging power is indicated by the magnitude of the angle β_1. The amount by which it separates blue from red is indicated by the angle α. The middle figure shows a flint glass lens, with a diverging power indicated by β_2, less than β_1: but it produces the same separation of red from blue as the other lens. The two together, in the third figure, do not separate blue from red, but possess a converging power $\beta_1 - \beta_2$.

of the best microscopic work has recently been accomplished by the use of monochromatic rays in the ultra-violet, rays which affect a photographic plate though they are invisible to the eye. Such for example is the photography of bacteria illustrated in Plate XIIIB.

These colour questions add greatly to the difficulties of the maker of optical instruments. The higher the magnification that is asked for, the greater the skill required to design the lenses. Our knowledge both of the very great and of the very small is derived largely from the employment of the telescope and the microscope: and we owe therefore a great debt to those who have devoted themselves to their perfection.

The Rainbow

The sparkling colours of the drops that remain hanging from leaves or fence wires when the sun comes out again after rain are due to a combination of refraction and reflection. In the retreating shower the colours gather together to make the rainbow. How this happens is explained in the two adjoining figures.

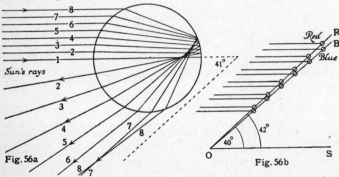

Fig. 56a. The circle represents a spherical drop of water. Parallel rays from the sun enter at the top of the figure, and emerge after two refractions and one reflection; the numbers show their separate courses. Most of the emerging rays are nearly parallel to a line making an angle of 41° with the original rays (actually 42° for red, 40° for blue).

Fig. 56b. Consequently, an observer at O, looking along any line which makes an angle of 42° with the direction of the sun (which is behind him) receives red from every drop in that line. These lines make a cone about O S as axis. A blue cone lies within the red.

It will be observed that the rainbow does not lie at any particular distance from the observer, though its colours lie in certain directions.

CHAPTER IV

THE ORIGINS OF COLOUR

The Principle of Resonance

WE have seen that colour is very generally produced by the destruction of colour. The light from the sun is a complex which can be analysed by a prism into a series of different qualities. These are distinguished by the eye as separate colours and by the physicist in his laboratory as different wave-lengths. We have seen something also of the curious mechanism of the eye whereby colours and mixtures of colours are perceived and passed on to the brain for interpretation.

Let us now consider more closely how this destruction of colour is accomplished. The light from the sun falls on the objects about us, leaves, grass, flowers, birds, insects, the earth itself and everywhere there is colour. Everywhere therefore, there must be destruction of colour. How is this accomplished? What is the process by which pigments fulfil their task?

It is well to observe at this point that, although the majority of the colorations surrounding us are due to pigments, there are certain other methods of producing colour which are extremely interesting and important and are moreover the cause of some of the most beautiful of all colour effects. They are generally considered under the two heads of diffraction and interference.

We will take them in their turn; but for the moment let us confine ourselves to the method of the pigment, which, at least quantitatively, is the principal cause of colour.

The secret lies in a principle known as that of resonance, the effects of which are indeed very common and easily to be observed. Let us take a very simple case, namely the action of one tuning fork upon another of like pitch. The two fixed on their appropriate sounding boxes stand side by side upon the table. One of them is strongly excited by drawing a bow across its prongs. It is allowed to sound for a few seconds and is then brought to silence by a touch of the finger. It is then found that the second fork is sounding, although it has never been touched: it has been set into motion by the first. After the second has been sounding a while, it may be stopped in its turn, whereupon the first may be found to have taken back some of the energy which it gave and to be sounding feebly.

It is essential that the tuning forks should be in tune. If a piece of wax is fastened to one of the prongs of either of them, the handing of energy backwards and forwards ceases, and the resonant effect no longer appears.

There are other examples in plenty. If one sits down before a piano and gently presses one of the notes so as to take the damper off the string, and then sings strongly the note, the string will resound and be heard when the voice ceases to sound. No other note will answer in the same way: the voice and the string must be in unison, except that a response may occur because each source of sound is not quite simple, containing overtones as well as the fundamental, and therefore there may be other opportunities of correspondence.

It has sometimes been the boast of a powerful singer that he can shatter a glass bowl without touching it by singing to it loudly on a note which the bowl would itself give out if struck.

But the commonest of all resonant effects in these days is the foundation of the working of wireless transmission. When we tune in we are availing ourselves directly of the resonance principle: we turn the knobs of our receiving set until the period or frequency of the electrical vibrations in its condensers and coils is exactly the same as that of the wave system coming from the sending station. The various stations emit waves of different frequencies, which differ exactly as one colour differs from another. Each station has its own special frequency, its own colour. Our receiving set is a 'pigment' absorbing a particular colour: and we have the power of changing the pigment until it absorbs the colour we want. The more perfect sets allow of the most accurate tuning, with the best response to the station looked for, and the most complete ignoring of all others.

If we ask ourselves why tuning should be so necessary and so effective we have only to think of some particular case where the motion is so slow that we can watch it. Imagine a child in a swing and someone who is setting the swing in motion. The swing has a natural period of to and fro movement: a frequency, meaning the number of swings in a minute or any other set time. If the impulses are given always at the right moment the amplitude of the swing continuously increases until the energy of each impulse is all used up in contending with the resistance of the air and other opposing forces. But if the impulses are given irregularly, or even regularly when the time between each impulse and the next is not that of the swing, the successive impulses defeat each other. One push may be given when the swing is receding, which is right, and another when it is coming, which will tend of course to stop the motion, and so on. A long series of regularly timed impulses will have no effect unless the timing is right, because the impulses will, at regular intervals, be for and against the movement.

When the one tuning fork sets the other in motion, each impulse is extremely feeble, being conveyed only by the air: but, the timing being perfect, the effects accumulate. When men march in step over a bridge it may be that there is danger because some vibrational period of the bridge coincides with that of the march: and the bridge may be weak and unable to stand it. Sometimes soldiers are told to break step when crossing. So it is with other cases of resonance, feeble impulses being effective when the timing is good.

The absorption of light of a particular wave-length by a pigment is also a resonance effect like all those that have been mentioned: and it particularly resembles that of wireless reception because it is electrical in nature and acts upon ether waves which differ only in length from those used in broadcasting. The wireless receiver absorbs the long ether waves, something in the pigment absorbs the short waves of light.

The wireless receiving set contains an arrangement of

electrical condensers, and coils of wire which are properly adjusted to each other. The atoms and molecules are the receiving sets of light: and this we know, even though we find it a difficult and complicated matter to compare them item by item with the larger sets. There are, however, general features of the atom and molecule considered as resonators which are extremely interesting, and these we may now examine. Let us think of some of the great colouring matters of the world.

There is just one preliminary point which we must consider because the connection between reception and absorption must be made clear. One tuning fork excites another: and some of the energy which it emits must be spent on the process. Just so every wireless receiving set absorbs a certain amount of energy from the ether. It may, by means of certain arrangements known to the wireless expert, be stimulated to the abstraction of energy from a store which is attached to its system, but that is another matter.

Imagine a tuning fork to be emitting energy in all directions. In one direction the sound waves come to a space where there are a great number of forks of the same pitch as the first. All of them are put into action to some extent, and energy of the waves is absorbed from the wave system in consequence. Clearly there is so much the less energy to go on in the original direction to which we have been confining our attention. It is true that the battery of receiving forks will all be emitting the same note, but the sum total of what they emit cannot be greater than what they took, and moreover they spread it in all directions. Thus there is certainly less to go on in the original direction. In other words, the battery of forks has acted as an absorber. If the first source had been comprised of two or three forks of different pitches beside the one that is of the same pitch as the battery of forks, the latter would not have picked any energy from the sound waves coming from the extra forks; the battery's action would be selective, absorbing one wave-length and allowing the others to pass on.

The analogy with the action of a pigment is obvious. The pigment is an assemblage of similar atoms and molecules all of which are capable of emitting and absorbing light of certain definite wave-lengths. We use the plural here, for the tuning fork is really far too simple a source of musical sound to represent the many possibilities of vibration which the atom or molecule possesses. The spectrum of white light which has gone through a space containing these complex vibrations must show a number of gaps.

The Vibrations of Atoms and Molecules

Atoms and molecules are of very small dimensions. We may introduce here the unit of length which is convenient for the expression of their magnitudes, the Angstrom unit, which is the hundred millionth of a centimetre, nearly the two hundred and fifty millionth part of an inch. Ninety-two different kinds of atom are known to exist. Molecules consist generally of a few atoms, two, three, four, and so on: it is a large molecule which is made of twenty or thirty or more atoms. The diameters of the atoms are of the order of one, two or three Angstrom units.

Various methods of investigation have led to fairly accurate measurements of these small magnitudes. Indeed, the methods of X-ray analysis can determine them with great precision, at least when the atoms and molecules are built into crystalline structures. The chemist has, in very many cases, been able to form an idea of the plan of the molecule: he can tell how the atoms are disposed with respect to each other, and the neighbours to which each atom is attached. This is done by laborious examination of chemical reactions, which term covers all those processes under which molecules of different kinds when brought together exchange atoms and form fresh combinations. This matter is very much too large for discussion here: it is sufficient to observe that such investigations are of the greatest importance, especially so in that branch of chemistry which concerns itself with the molecules particularly involved in the structure of living organisms. The properties of the molecule depend on the arrangement of the atoms, as might well be expected: just as the nature of a house depends on how its various constituents, bricks, planks, tiles, etc., are disposed. The X-rays have recently come to the aid of the chemist in this work: we shall see later how they may add definition and fresh knowledge to that which the chemical methods reveal.

Now, although we cannot describe the mode in which a molecule vibrates as easily as we can describe the movements of a tuning fork, yet we find that we are able, in some cases, to see certain connections between the 'notes' of a molecule and its structure. And as it is very interesting and often of industrial importance to discover any such connections, the molecules that especially give rise to colour have been studied with great care. The points that are most examined are the notes, or natural frequencies, and the composition and form of the molecule.

Chlorophyll

Let us begin with the chlorophyll molecule, one of the most interesting, and from the point of view of the life processes, the most important of all molecules. It is extremely complicated, and the study of it has not gone very far. But it is not unnatural to take it first, because it colours for us all the world of vegetation, and more than that, it takes in for us the energy of the sun's rays and converts it to our use. On the one hand it fills our eyes with beauty whenever we go out of doors, on the other hand it helps the world to make the first step in the life process. Moreover, coal and oil on which we depend so much are stores of energy derived by chlorophyll from the sun's rays in past ages.

If we throw a spectrum upon the screen in the usual way, using a prism to open out the rays from the sun or from an electric arc, and if we then place a cell containing chlorophyll in the path of the rays – a preparation of nettle leaves gives us chlorophyll readily and conveniently – we find that the long wave-lengths are strongly absorbed, except for a narrow band in the deep red (Plate XIVG). Other fainter bands are to be seen in other parts of the spectrum, and the extreme blue has disappeared. But it is the absorption of long wave-lengths that is important. The chlorophyll molecule responds to this particular range of wave-lengths in the sun's light, and so takes up energy. The chemist has shown that so fortified, if the term may be used in a broad sense, the chlorophyll molecule can combine with the ubiquitous molecule of carbon dioxide (carbonic acid). In this way are formed the 'carbo-hydrates' – starches and sugars – which are the foundations of the activity of plants. As we eat the plants, or eat the animals which eat the plants, we also derive our activities from the absorption of the red rays of chlorophyll.

Surely one of the most remarkable of all observations is that which shows us this one particular molecule as playing so great a part. It is the same in all plants: it is known indeed that there are two different forms of it, but, apart from that, every plant of every description makes use of the same molecule for the same purpose. Our interest is increased if we take into account that haemoglobin which plays so important a function in animal life is of an allied structure. There is some great secret, not yet known, which is involved in this universal use of one particular form of molecule. Its composition is known: it contains fifty-five atoms of carbon, seventy-two of hydrogen, five of oxygen, four of nitrogen and one of magnesium; truly a complex affair. But only a very little has been discovered as to the arrangement of these atoms, which remains a problem of outstanding interest.

The Colours of Flowers

The colours of the flowers must attract us next. Here again the whole scheme depends on a small number of basic forms, though of course there must, in this case, be many derivatives, since the colours are of such infinite variety. One of the most important of these forms is that of carotin, a colouring matter which in one of its varieties was extracted from carrots a hundred years ago. The molecule is compounded of forty carbon atoms and fifty-six hydrogen atoms, but little is known of the manner in which they are linked together. Another plant pigment is xanthophyll, which differs from carotin only, so far as composition is concerned, in the possession

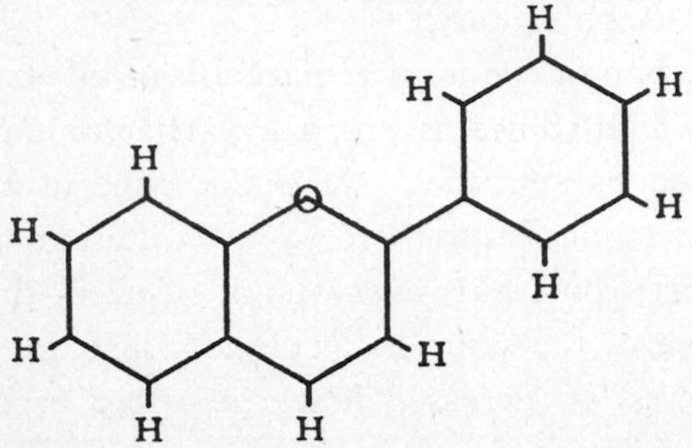

Fig. 57. The diagram shows the arrangement of the atoms in the primitive of the anthocyanin molecules which give colours to the flowers.

of two oxygen atoms in addition to those already named. These two and their variants are mainly responsible for the yellows and reds of flowers. The former is found for example in daffodils, cowslips, and dandelions; the latter in marigolds, buttercups, celandine and sunflowers. These colouring matters are found in the leaves of plants as well as in the flowers, and when the chlorophyll disappears as the year advances they remain to give us the colours of autumn. Quite lately it has been found that Vitamin A is produced from carotin by the action of ultra-violet light.

Then there are very interesting substances known as the anthocyanins which also provide the colours of many flowers. In this case the structure and composition are both known and it is possible to observe how certain changes in form produce changes in colour. The standard structure is shown in Fig. 57, where the curious linkings of carbon and oxygen into six-sided rings is a feature of the plan. Carbon atoms lie at every junction of straight lines, except at the one marked O where there is an atom of oxygen: they are not specially indi-

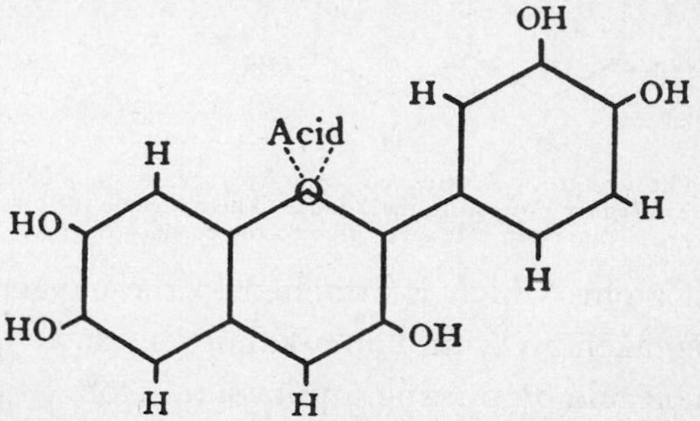

Fig 58. The anthocyanin which gives red to the rose is formed from that of Fig. 57 by attaching an acid group loosely to the oxygen atom and replacing hydrogens by hydroxyl groups (hydrogen + oxygen) at certain points. The molecule is now acidic.

cated in the figure. Hydrogens are attached at the points marked H. The order in which the atoms are linked together has been determined by chemical methods.

The arrangement is probably planar, but there is no certain knowledge of this. Certain other molecules which contain hexagonal carbon rings – benzene rings – have been shown by X-ray methods to be planar, and it has also been shown in those cases that the hexagon is regular in form, having a length of side of 1.42 Angstrom units. (One AU = 1/100,000,000 of a centimetre.)

Anthocyanins are responsible for a large number of

the reds, mauves, purples, and blues. In Fig. 58 for
instance is the variety that gives its colour to the rose: the
principal addition to the basic form of Fig. 57 is the acid

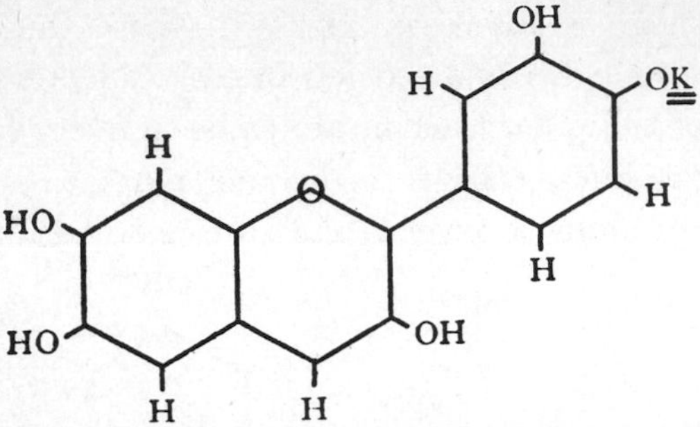

Fig. 59. The acid group is removed and a hydrogen of one of the hydroxyl
groups is replaced by potassium marked κ. The molecule is now alkaline in
character. It gives blue to the cornflower.

group of atoms which is attached to the oxygen atom.
If this be taken away and an alkaline character be given
to the molecule by putting a potassium atom in place of
the hydrogen at one end of the molecule, we have the
anthocyanin that gives the blue colour to the cornflower
(Fig. 59). In some parts of the country the children
plant the blue wild hyacinth near to ants' nests,

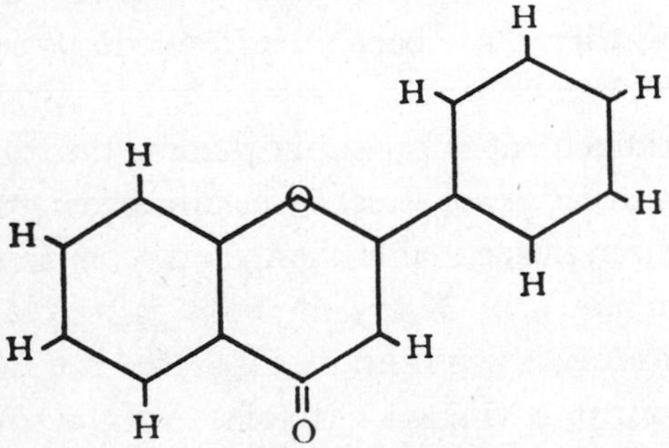

Fig. 60. The primitive of anthoxanthin is formed from that of anthocyanin
by the addition of an oxygen atom, strongly bound to one of the carbons in
the middle ring, replacing a hydrogen atom at that point.

where the formic acid turns the blue of the flower into red.

There is a slight modification of the anthocyanin skeleton molecule as shown in Fig. 60 where an oxygen atom has been attached at one point. This causes the molecule to be soluble in water; it is responsible for the colour of the primrose and presumably this is the reason why primroses become so colourless when wet.

Dyes

From time immemorial men have extracted dyes from plants, but curiously enough they have rarely used the natural colouring matters of leaves and flowers. They have made use of constituents of the plant which play no part in the coloration of the plant itself. The natural colours are too fugitive. The alterations in hue which follow the changing seasons are proper to the scheme of Nature, but man looks for something more lasting when he sets out to decorate his implements or his house or himself. So for example, he has extracted indigo and its near relation woad from the roots of certain plants which he learnt to cultivate. From these and their derivatives the dyer has made many well known colours.

The structure of the indigo molecule is well known: it is shown in Fig. 61. Since it was finally determined in 1883 by A von Baeyer, its synthetic manufacture has entirely replaced the older and more laborious process of extraction from the plant. There is a curious and interesting feature in the manner of its use. Indigo itself is insoluble in water: which is indeed a strong recommendation to its use since it is to provide the colouring matter of objects which will be exposed to the weather. But the dyeing process requires a solution into which the textile material may be dipped. To get over the difficulty, the dyer treats the indigo chemically in a way which results in the addition of hydrogen atoms

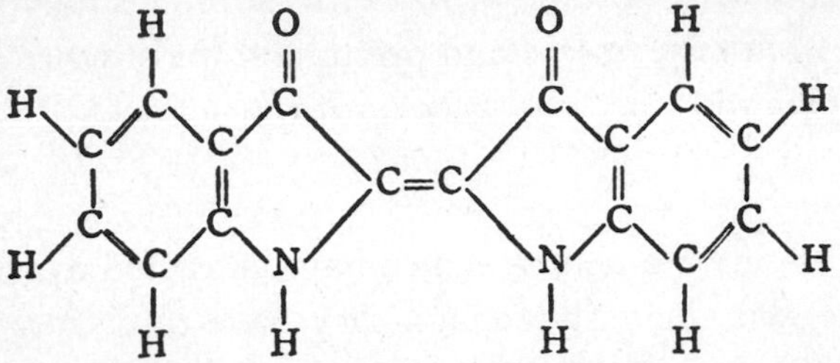

Fig. 61. The indigo molecule, drawn to show the result of the determination of its atomic arrangement by chemical methods.

to the molecule (Fig. 62). So changed the molecule has the power of attaching itself to a water molecule: that is to say the indigo becomes soluble in water.

At the same time it becomes colourless, which illustrates very well a point we have been trying to make, namely, that the molecular absorption of light is of the nature of a resonance. We saw that the pitch of a tuning fork was altered when wax was attached to one or

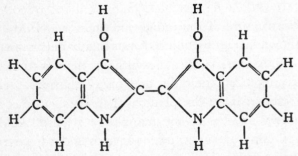

Fig. 62. The indigo molecule, altered so as to become soluble.

both of the prongs. We loaded the fork, and the vibrations were therefore made to slow down. So in the same way, if there is any parallelism, we should expect that the 'note' or 'notes' of a molecule could be altered by weighting it, that is to say by adding atoms in the proper places. The dye chemist does in fact experiment with such additions: he tries to find out what he should add and where he should add it. He is of course bound to secure 'fastness' at the same time: the ordinary experiences to which his dyed material is to be subjected must not loosen or remove any additions that he has made.

The range of visible wave-lengths is very small: and it is easy to shift the note to a very different part of the spectrum, or even to push it out altogether. This is what has happened to the indigo molecule when it is made soluble in water. It no longer absorbs the long waves and leaves the blue: it leaves them all, and the solution is colourless.

This, however, is no hindrance during the dyeing. The material is dipped into the solution of the indigo and the dye is attached to the fibres. Now, the hydrogen atoms which have been added to the indigo molecule are very easily removed again by exposure to the air. As soon as the material is removed from the dye-bath the molecule begins to return to the normal form which gives the indigo colour. The stuff is then fast to moisture, and the dyer has achieved his purpose.

The woad with which our ancestors decorated their bodies two thousand years ago, and the Imperial purple of Rome which was extracted from the shell fish

Murex are based on the same molecular structure as indigo.

The colours of leaves and flowers are, of course, the most widely displayed of all that we see in the world about us: except those of the sky and the sea which we shall consider presently. These latter, like the colours of the blue distance and of the sunset, are not due to pigments and are to be explained in a totally different way. There are also the colours of the earths and rocks, some of them so brilliant that they have been made use of as paints; these also derive their colour from the absorption process, and therefore are to be classed with the pigments we have been considering.

Diffraction

But now we must break new ground, and go on to observe certain ways of providing colour, which differ entirely from those methods of partial absorption which we have just been examining.

We took note before of the remarkable fact that a ray of light pursues its way with little loss to either side, and we saw that it was not very easy to understand how this might be if light were to be considered as a form of wave motion. Newton had indeed made this his principal objection to the wave theory. Experiments with water waves such as we may perform on the ripple tank always show a certain amount of sideways spreading: and it might be thought, with Newton, that this effect should manifest itself in the case of light also in such an obvious way that the wave theory ought to be given up. But, as a matter of fact, that which seemed a fatal objection has turned out to be most striking evidence in its favour. Closer examination has shown that sideways spreading may become very small and difficult to detect if the length of the wave is small compared to the width of the ray. In the case of light the ratio of the former of the two quantities to the latter is often very small indeed, so that the spreading is quite difficult to observe, fortunately for the purposes of vision.

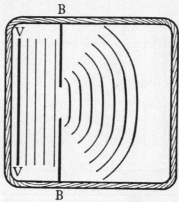

Fig. 63. Ripples started by the vibrating bar v move up to the barrier B in which there is a relatively wide opening. The continuation of the advance of the waves shows for some time the form of the opening.

This point is of the greatest importance to our theories of light. Let us therefore examine it carefully and guide ourselves by experiment.

If we set two barriers in the tank (Fig. 63) leaving a space between them and make ripples roll up to the opening and pass through, we see at once that there is always some of this sideways spreading. The waves on the farther side are to some extent continuations of the original wave motion on the nearer side and are parallel to them. On either side of the new wave system there are what we may call wings which show the sideways spreading of which we are speaking. The wider the opening the more important is the middle portion which implies a regular onward movement of the original system of waves, and the less important are the wings. If we make the opening very small, the wings and the centre become merely semi-circles, and the disturbance

Fig. 64. In this case the opening in the barrier is relatively small, and the continuation of the advance of the waves takes the form of semicircular ripples.

after it gets through the hole spreads equally in all directions, as in Fig. 64.

When we speak of the size of the opening, we must mean its size relative to the length of the wave. An opening which may be large for short waves, may be a small opening and lead to the semi-circular spreading of Fig. 64 when the waves are long.

We cannot reproduce on the tank the proportions which hold in the case of a ray of light. Our ripples are always too large for our openings. In the case of light an opening an inch wide is some thirty thousand times as large as the wave-length: we can easily imagine how negligible is the wing portion as compared with the centre. It would be necessary to enlarge our tank thousands of times and to open in the same proportion the opening between the barriers before we began to observe effects which copied those of light. We do, however, learn from the tank experiments that sideways spreading must always take place to some extent: and we realise that under ordinary circumstances we shall see nothing of it in the case of a ray of light. Under extraordinary circumstances such as we can produce in a laboratory we can observe it; we are able, in other words, to show that light can turn a corner when the conditions are right. Moreover, the tank experiments help us to see that since the wave-length plays a part in this effect, the long waves and the short waves may not turn the corner with equal facility, and colour might so come into existence. This is indeed the case, but as the whole effect is not easy to see under ordinary conditions, the separations into colour are still less obvious.

But now if we proceed to make special arrangements for our experiments in the tank we may find our way to an explanation of why the colorations in the case of light can become very strong. We place in the ripple tank a barrier pierced with a number of openings which for our preliminary experiment may be arranged in any way and need not be all of the same size. When ripples are made to advance towards this barrier, and in portions to break through it, we observe that the wave systems that emerge on the further side recombine in a short time and reform the old front. Each system that emerges from an opening would spread away in a semi-circular system as in Fig. 65, but it merges its actions with those of all the others and so in the end a straight fronted wave appears and progresses in the original direction. The object of this experiment is to show the combination of semi-circular wave systems into one straight-fronted system.

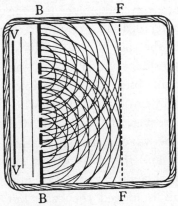

Fig. 65. When the ripples (Fig. 64) spread from a number of openings a front is eventually formed, indicated by the dotted line, which is parallel to the original wave front.

Now imagine the first barrier to be replaced by another in which the openings are regularly spaced. They need not be the same size, but it is convenient to make them so. We can draw a diagram which will enable us to tell what will happen in this case: more easily indeed than we can observe in the actual experiment because the tank is hardly large enough. This diagram is reproduced in Fig. 66. Although it looks complicated it consists only of sets of semi-circles drawn about the centres of the openings. Each shows how a set of semi-circular waves would spread away if the opening were

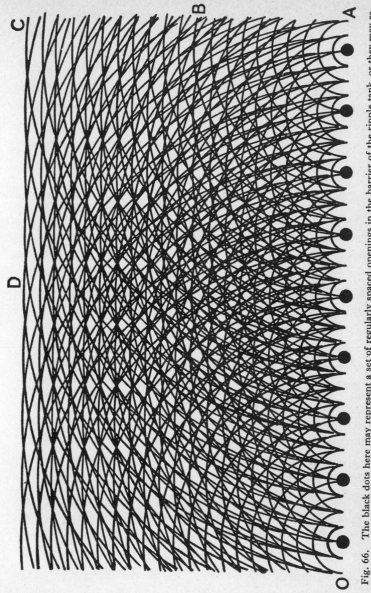

Fig. 66. The black dots here may represent a set of regularly spaced openings in the barrier of the ripple tank, or they may represent a set of particles, evenly spaced, which scatter the incident light in the form of circular ripples (or spherical if we extend the treatment to the three-dimensional case). The waves are advancing from below, and their front is parallel to O A. The wave-front D C is formed as already explained Fig. 65. Here other wave-fronts are formed also. To see them look along the diagram obliquely in the directions O A, O B, O C, and O D in turn. There are no other wave-fronts but these. (Diagram by W. T. Astbury.)

131

the only one in the barrier. In the actual case the sets are compounded into one system, and as in the former experiment a train of waves is formed which may be looked on as a continuation of the original train, but of less energy. The front of this train is parallel to the original wave-front and gathers definition as it moves away from the barrier. So far the experiment is exactly the same, except that the spacings of the openings are now uniform, as that of Fig. 65.

But now a new effect appears, which can only occur when the openings are equally spaced. In addition to the wave-front which carries on the old line of advance, another wave-front forms itself in an oblique direction parallel to the line OB in the diagram. It is formed by a combination of waves belonging to the separate semi-circular systems: these waves did not, however, pass through the openings at the same moment, but at successive intervals. The front touches, for example, the first circle belonging to the first hole, the second belonging to the second hole, and so on. It can be most easily observed in the diagram if the page of the book is held nearly on a level with the eye, so that the diagram is seen in strong perspective, and the line of sight is directed parallel to OB. The diagram of Fig. 67, which is an extract from the fuller diagram of Fig. 68 may help to make this clearer. Since a new wave-front forms in this way a diversion of energy in a new direction takes place. We have what is usually called a diffracted beam. The effect is constantly observed in the optical laboratory, and indeed is the foundation of a certain very accurate means of analysing light, as we shall see presently.

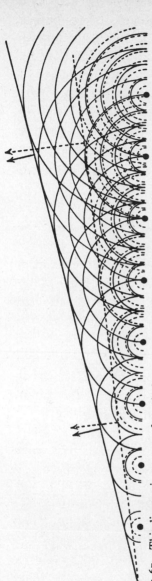

Fig. 67. This diagram is an extract from the last, showing the formation of the diffracted waves of the first order. It also shows how the direction of diffraction depends upon the length of the wave. The shorter waves are related to the longer in approximately the same way as the blue waves to the red.

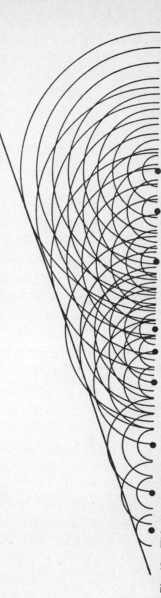

Fig. 68. This diagram shows that a diffracted set of waves is not formed unless the centres (black dots) are spaced evenly. If a straight line is drawn, as in the figure, to touch some of the wave crests which the circles represent, it goes between others. Thus some of the ripples would cause a crest on the front and some a hollow, and in the aggregate there is mutual destruction. The 'interference' between the separate sets of ripples is more fully discussed in what follows.

By turning the diagram round in its own plane and looking in succession along the lines OC and OD one may see that there are other directions in which wave-fronts are formed after the disturbance has passed through the screen, and other diversions of energy. We speak of the diffracted pencils of the first, second, third order, and so on. In the diagram the wave-length is one quarter of the spacing of the openings: for which reason, as the diagram shows, there are three diffracted pencils on each side of the original direction.

Nothing of this sort happens if the openings are not spaced equally along the barrier. Only when the spacing is regular can the straight wave-front touch a selection of the semi-circular waves and be the result of their joint action. This is illustrated in Fig. 68.

It is to be observed that the deflection of a diffracted ray of light is less the smaller the wave-length and the further apart the openings are spaced. In Fig. 67 the diffraction effect of the first order is shown for waves of two different lengths. A pair of photographs shown on Plate XVA supply a further illustration of this point. These show diffraction effects of many orders.

The optical experiment is easily shown. A set of parallel straight lines is drawn on a piece of glass, some thousands to the centimetre, the whole covering a rectangular portion of the glass a few centimetres each way. This is known as a diffraction grating. It is an extremely difficult matter to rule a really good grating: and the best come from a very few ruling engines which are well known. The gratings prepared by the late Professor Rowland of Baltimore have a great reputation.

There is an excellent ruling engine at the National Physical Laboratory.

The light from the arc emerges from the lantern through a narrow slit, which is focused upon the screen. The slit and the lens have not been mentioned in the theory as explained above, but are necessities if the images upon the screen are to be clear and bright. Supposing that the slit is vertical and the grating is placed so that its lines are parallel to the slit, then Fig. 69 will repre-

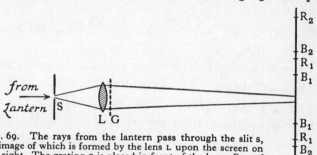

Fig. 69. The rays from the lantern pass through the slit s, an image of which is formed by the lens L upon the screen on the right. The grating G is placed in front of the lens. Part of the light is then diffracted. Images of the slit appear in blue at B1, B2 . . . and in red at R1, R2. . . . Thus spectra are formed. The spectrum of the first order lies between B1 and R1; of the second between B2 and R2 and so on.

sent a horizontal section of the arrangement, except that the wave-lengths and the spacings of the grating cannot be drawn as fine as they should be. The clear spaces of the glass correspond to the openings in the screen of Fig. 66 and the rulings, being opaque, to the parts of the barrier between the openings. The various wavelengths are then diffracted in different directions, the red most, and the blue least, and a spectrum appears upon the screen showing the same array of colour as the prism produced for us before. Moreover, the spectrum is repeated in the second and higher orders, and each time it is more extended and the colours are better separated.

This method of obtaining a spectrum has the great merit of informing us of the wave-length of each diffracted colour. The diagram of Fig. 67 shows that there is a relation between the wave-length, the spacing of the grating and the angle which the diffracted ray makes with the original direction. We can observe the last factor, the second was settled during the ruling, and so the value of the first quantity can be deduced. In this way the wave-lengths are determined with extraordinary accuracy.

The grating may be ruled on a piece of good reflecting metal, as for example the speculum metal that is used for the mirrors of reflecting telescopes. The light is then reflected from the grating surface, and exactly the same results are obtained as when the light was transmitted through the grating ruled on glass.

The colours of the wing cases of certain beetles, some of the colours of butterflies' wings and of birds' feathers, as for example the colours of the peacock's tail, are diffraction effects. The peacock's feathers show no bright colour when looked through; they show only a brown.

Sometimes diffraction colours of this same sort are obtained by the special treatment of a material. The colours of mother-of-pearl are due to the presence of fine groovings on the polished surface. The substance has been formed in layers and the process of manufacture cuts across them and leaves a set of parallel ridges. If an impression be taken of the mother-of-pearl in wax, the colours appear on the wax also: the coloration is due to form, not to pigment. The colours of sky and sea are also largely due to diffraction, but the manner of their production must be given special consideration. We shall discuss them later.

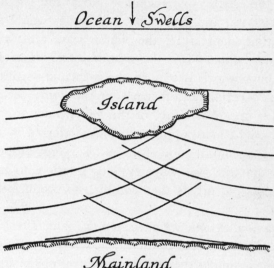

Ocean ↓ Swells

Island

Mainland

Fig. 70. Ocean waves sweep round the two sides of an island and combine as shown.

Interference

It will be well now to examine a different but allied cause of colour, known as the principle of interference; allied, because it also can be explained as a direct consequence of the wave theory. It is a characteristic effect of wave motion which we may often observe on the surface of the sea, when two sets of waves sweep through one another. There is an islet off the South Australian coast (Fig. 70) which divides the swells coming up from the Antarctic and causes two wave systems to sweep round it and cross one another obliquely as they approach the shore. It is curious to watch the result. Where crest meets crest the water leaps up in spray: where hollow meets hollow there is a double depth. When the crest of one system would at some spot raise the water up, and a trough of the other would at the same time depress it, the water stays still, neither rising nor falling. It is this mutual interference of crest and trough which has given the principle its title: but there is a certain insufficiency in the name because it refers to one phase only of the general action, which action might more appropriately be referred to as the addition or combination of waves. It is only at specified points that the two wave systems interfere to mutual destruction, at others they combine to produce double effects.

On a smaller scale we have seen the same effect in the ripple tank: the form of the surface of the water at any moment is simply the sum of the forms of the separate wave systems. There is therefore nothing in the interference phenomena which we may not observe and watch whenever we look down at the surface of moving water. At sea, for example, we may see a set of ripples riding on the surface of a larger wave, and this again on an ocean swell. Any one set moves on the curved surface of the larger set as if the latter had been plane.

When therefore Thomas Young lecturing at the Royal Institution in the first years of the nineteenth century enunciated the principle of interference and applied it to explain certain remarkable optical effects his genius seized hold of an effect which any one may see at any time.

The principle does not differ in reality from that of diffraction, both being consequences of the additive character of wave motions, but the two are generally distinguished from one another, the distinctions applying rather to the nature of the effects examined under the two heads.

Let us take as an example of the effects of interference the colours of the soap film. Young himself chose the same example, and gave its explanation in his book on Natural Philosophy.

The soap film is a thin layer of water held together by the mutual attractions of the molecules of which soap is composed. It is transparent to light. When a ray of light falls upon the film, a portion is reflected at the first surface it encounters, and another portion at the second. The two subsequently move away together and they interfere in the same sense as the two wave systems that swung round the islet in the manner already described. There is, however, a peculiar regularity in the soap film reflection. The set of waves reflected from the first surface is added to the second set which has traversed the film twice, and has therefore lagged behind a little. The two necessarily overlap: and where crest meets crest there is a double effect and so on.

Now the lag of one reflected system behind the other depends upon how much ground is lost in crossing the film twice: and this again depends upon the thickness of the film and the direction in which it is crossed. The lag may be reckoned in wave-lengths of the particular

quality of light. Suppose that it amounts to a whole
number of wave-lengths, one, two, three or more. Then

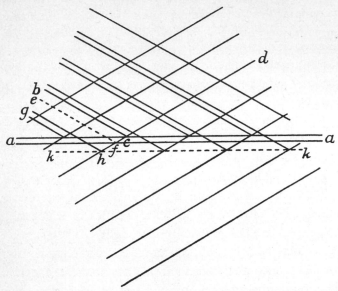

Fig. 71. A train of waves falls upon the thin film *a a*. The film may be of
any transparent material. The waves strike the upper surface and are reflected as shown, as for example *b c d* where *b c* is the reflected portion and
the part *c d* has not yet met the film. If *c d* is the crest of one part of the
wave, *b c* is the crest of the other. The waves pass on, losing only a part of
their energy by reflection at the first surface, and meet the second. Here
they lose half a wave-length in the act of reflection, as explained in the text.
The dotted line *e f* shows where the crest of the reflected wave would have
been if the reflection at the second face had been of the same character as
that at the first. The loss of the half wave-length puts the reflected wave
back to *g h*. Reflection takes place as if at the surface shown by the dotted
line *k k*: the extra delay has the effect of adding apparently to the thickness
of the film.

the two sets of waves run absolutely together, crest and
crest, trough and trough. They add together and make
a wave of double the extent of movement up and down:
and therefore, it may be shown, of four times the energy
of either one of the reflected rays.

It must now be observed that it is necessary to add

half a wave-length to the lag calculated geometrically. This is due to a certain physical effect. One reflection takes place in air at the surface of water, and the other in water at the surface of air. The two differ in character: the latter loses half a wave-length in the act of reflection as shown in the diagram (Fig. 71). The effect is the same as that which has similar results in the case of organ pipes: where the reflections of the sound wave from open and closed ends show a like difference. It may easily be seen that some such allowance must be made, for if the film were reduced to vanishing, the two reflections would then be exactly in step, and yet there could be no reflection if the film were not there. The half wave-length loss accounts perfectly for the absence of any reflection when the film is very thin, because it throws the two exactly out of step: the crests of one reflection fitting into the hollows of the other reflection, mutual interference and destruction being the result. It is a matter of ordinary observation that a very thin soap film reflects no colour: this part of the film is generally described as the black spot, though with care it can be made so large that the term 'spot' is quite inadequate.

If therefore all the causes of lag amount in all to a whole number of wave-lengths there is a strong reflection. But the same lag will, in respect to some other wave-lengths, amount to a whole number and a half. In that case the two reflected pencils destroy each other entirely, and there is no reflection of the light of that particular wave-length; all the energy involved in it passes on unchecked. Thus the film sorts out the various colours, reflecting some and transmitting others: it is coloured when looked at from either side.

The colour reflected at a particular angle of reflection depends, as we have seen, upon the thickness of the film. If a circular wire frame is dipped in soap solution and then held in a vertical position the liquid will gradually drain downwards, so that the thickness increases with the depth. Consequently the colours appear in horizontal bands. One of the most beautiful of all optical experiments is provided when a fine jet of air is projected obliquely against the film, setting up whirls on the surface. Just as in whirlpools in open water the rotation about the centre causes the liquid to move outwards to the circumference. The colours then form themselves in ovals about the centre. Very rich colours are quickly obtained in this way, because the whirling and blowing tend to thin the film, and as we know from experience the colours of a soap bubble improve as it becomes thinner and are at their best just before the black spot forms or the bubble bursts.

The explanation of this enrichment is not far to seek, and is of especial interest because Young wrote about it, and figured it in colour in his book (Plate ID).

Suppose that the lag of the one reflection with respect to the other is two thousandths of a millimetre. The red wave-length which is 0.8 thousandths does not appear in the reflected beam because $0.8 \times 2.5 = 2$; so that the lag is two and a half of such wave-lengths. Two other wave-lengths within the visible spectrum will also be absent, viz. 0.57 thousandths and 0.44 because $0.57 \times 3.5 = 0.44 \times 4.5 = 2$. That is to say the lag is equal to three and a half wave-lengths and four and a half wave-lengths respectively. In all there will be gaps in the deep red (0.8), the yellow (0.57), and the blue (0.45): no other gaps fall within the visible spectrum. The colour of the reflected light will be a compound of what is left.

Suppose that the lag is larger, say four thousandths of a millimetre. There will then be a greater number of gaps in the spectrum of the reflected light, and they will be less widely spaced. We have 4 equal to 0.73 × 5.5, 0.62 × 6.5, 0.53 × 7.5, 0.47 × 8.5, and 0.42 × 9.5: and these wave-lengths, 0.73, 0.62, 0.53, . . . all fall within the spectrum. Now when the spectrum is deprived of several portions equally spaced, it is found by experiment that the compounding of the rest is only feebly coloured. It is in fact only when the film is so thin that the lag is only half a wave-length or one and a half wave-lengths, quite a small number, that the coloration is strong.

Young showed this by examining the light reflected from the soap film by means of a prism. He narrowed down the light by means of a vertical slit and placed his prism in the path of the light which the slit allowed to pass, obtaining a spectrum just as we obtained one from the light of the arc. The result is shown in Plate ID, which is reproduced from his original drawing. The picture is turned through a right angle. It will be observed that the gaps, taken as a whole, present the appearance of diffuse bands running obliquely across the picture. The reason is that the gaps are few and far between in the spectrum of the top of the film (left), and numerous towards the bottom where the film is thicker (right).

Young used this simple explanation of the colours of thin films in support of the wave theory. Newton himself had foreshadowed the explanation, but he had thought of it only as an auxiliary and complicated hypothesis, which he required to complete his theory of corpuscles. Young, by thus establishing the interference principle, made a great step forward in the showing that the wave was sufficient for the phenomena that were then known. An example of the colours of thin films is shown in Plate IA.

We do not see on a great scale the simple colour effects of the thin film, but in minor ways they occur often enough. They account for the colours of tempered steels which are coated with thin films of iron oxides. They make the bright colours which appear when petrol or other oils spread in thin sheets over water surfaces. We see them in cracks of glass or other transparent substances: and they are prettily shown in a form known as Newton's rings when a lens is laid upon a sheet of glass so that there is a thin film of air between the two bodies, and, as the thickness of the film increases from the centre outwards the colours appear in the form of concentric rings, the centre being at the point of contact.

The principle of interference appears again in a different part of our field when it explains the X-ray effects by which the structures of crystalline structures are determined. And yet again it is of importance to the electrical engineers who have to deal with the summation of alternating currents of electricity, which surge like waves along the conducting wires.

The principle has a very strong application to acoustics

accounting for beats and other phenomena of musical sounds. When the tuning note is given on the wireless there are points in the room where crests of sound waves continuously meet troughs and there is comparative silence, and again, there are places where the sound is always strong. The interference takes place between the original sound and its reflections from the walls of the room and from objects in the room. As we move our heads about we hear the consequent variations in intensity.

CHAPTER V

THE COLOURS OF THE SKY

The Selective Scattering of Light

THE various colours of the sky, its fundamental blue, the haloes which sometimes surround the sun and the moon, the red and gold and green of sunrises and sunsets, these and other effects are due to reactions between the waves of light and the molecules and particles of various sorts which compose the atmosphere and float in it. There is no colouring matter in the atmosphere, nothing that behaves like a pigment which absorbs certain colours and allows others to pass on. There is separation of colours but no destruction. It was at one time suggested that the air contained, or was itself, a blue gas, which absorbed the red. But if this were so the sun and moon and stars would appear more and more blue as they drew near to the horizon and their rays had to traverse a greater quantity of air before reaching the eye. We should see a paler blue overhead and a darker blue lower down: which is not the case.

The wave theory suggests a better explanation. Light must be scattered by particles floating in the air just as the waves of the sea are turned aside and scattered by rocks that rise above its surface. The short waves of light that compose the blue end of the spectrum must be more easily turned aside than the longer red waves, just as ripples are turned aside by a rock over which the larger waves heave themselves and then go on. Thus a separation takes place and colour is produced. On this hypothesis we should expect that the light of the sun would incline towards yellow or even red towards sunrise and sunset, because the longer traverse of the air would remove the blue rays more completely. At the same time the blue that is turned to one side will make the blue of the sky.

Examples of this effect are very common. The smoke rising from a chimney looks blue against a dark background, especially when the particles of carbon that cause the scattering are very small, as when they come from a wood fire or from a coal fire which has not been recently renewed. Carbon is of course black in the lump, but the scattering by the very fine particles in the smoke is more effective than the pigmentary absorption. For a good blue the particles should be smaller than the wave-length of light, and in such a case the absorption effects are relatively small. If, on the other hand, the smoke is viewed against a bright background of luminous cloud, or even against the sun itself, the colour that comes through is brown or red.

The smoke from the burning end of a cigarette is blue as it rises in the air, but that which has been in the mouth is grey. In the latter case the particles have been covered with moisture from the warm breath and the increase in size is responsible for a more pronounced scattering of the longer waves.

A red light carries better than a whiter light in a

misty atmosphere, because the water particles do not scatter the long waves of the red so much as those of the blue. The details of a misty view can be photographed with greater ease if a yellow glass is placed before the lens, since the scattered blue is then absorbed. The motor driver is apt to be dazzled by the scattered rays that return to his eyes, and red glasses are often placed before the head lamps in order to cut out the shorter waves. So also red flares are used to help the traffic in a fog. Recent experiment has shown however that the use of red light is of doubtful benefit because fog particles are large enough to scatter all the visible wave-lengths. The infra-red waves which we shall presently consider are long enough to escape scattering.

Molecular Scattering

Thus the wave theory can easily account for the appearance of colour when rays traverse an atmosphere containing fine particles. These might be dust or they might be particles of water vapour: both have been suggested as the effective agents. Tyndall ascribed the blue of the sky to the latter. But the late Lord Rayleigh showed by calculation that it was unnecessary, in the search for a cause, to look further than the molecules of the air itself. The air molecules are of course, very small, much smaller than the wave-length of light, but the cumulative action of a vast number of minute amounts of scattering by the separate molecules is enough to account for the light that we receive from the blue sky. Near the surface of the earth there is much matter in suspension in the atmosphere and scattering is due to this also. But the earth's dust cloud does not rise above 3,000 feet, and at the Mount Wilson Observatory in California 5,000 feet above sea level it has been possible to measure the intensity of the light from the sky, and to compare the result with the figure deduced from Rayleigh's theory. A complete agreement is found to exist.

The light that is scattered sideways from sun light which penetrates the lower levels is not so pure a blue as in the upper levels where there is no dust to add longer wave-lengths to those which are due to the air molecules themselves. In northern latitudes, particularly in this country, there is generally much moisture in the air, and the blue of the sky is pale and watery as compared with the deep blue of countries in lower latitudes. These countries do not always enjoy the brilliant blue nevertheless: sometimes the hot dry wind rushes down and raises clouds of dust, until the blue has gone and the sky has become colourless and darkened. Then, it may be, the rain pours down carrying the dust with it, and literally washing the sky.

Tyndall used to show a beautiful experiment in illustration of this theory that the blue was due to fine particles in suspension. A glass tube about three feet long was mounted as shown in Plate XVB. Its ends were closed by glass plates, so that a beam of light could be sent through it. It was first evacuated, and then filled with a mixture of air, hydrochloric acid and the vapour of butyl nitrite. In a few minutes chemical reactions caused the formation of very fine particles which remained suspended in the gas. The particles were uniform in size, which was an important point. They scattered the blue to one side, and as they began to form and then grow, an observer viewing the tube from one side was aware first of a faint deep blue which gradually grew stronger and lighter in shade as the particles increased in size. According to his own enthusiastic description: 'We produce a blue which rivals, if it does not transcend, that of the deepest and purest Italian sky.'

In another form of this experiment, which is very easily shown, a glass tank is filled with a solution of very dilute thiosulphate of soda. A ray of light goes through the tank and is projected upon the screen where it forms a white circle; dilute hydrochloric acid is added, and particles of sulphur then separate out in a minute or two, and grow in size: and as they do so the colour of the light that gets through the tank becomes yellow and then red, and the white circle is changed first into a yellow sun and then into a red sun at setting. Meanwhile the water in the tank is first a blue and in the end is grey like a fog. A coloured photograph of this effect is shown in Plate XIVH.

Tyndall believed that, if he removed all the dust and all the vapour from his glass tube, there was nothing left to scatter the light, and that nothing could be seen, from one side of the ray, as it went along the tube. In this he was mistaken, but his experiment showed well the existence of scattering by particles and the dependence of the scattered colour upon the particle size.

The present Lord Rayleigh pointed out that it should be possible to observe the scattering of light by air molecules even in a tube of the size employed by Tyndall. He pointed out that there is light from the sky even when it is lit by the moon only, and therefore that, as sunlight is half a million times stronger than moonlight, the light scattered by sunlight in traversing an amount of air equal to two millionths of an atmosphere should be as easily seen as the moonlit sky: in fact, that the scattering of a few inches of air should be enough to be visible. This proved to be the case, when the experiment was made with the appropriate optical instruments.

Much of course of the gorgeous colour of the sun and sky in the morning and evening is due to scattering by dust and water vapour superimposed upon the effects due to the air molecules. Sometimes the smoke of a fire, a bush fire perhaps, adds a deep red to the coloration. When Krakatoa ejected quantities of the finest dust into the air at its eruption half a century ago, the colours of the sky all over the world were strangely beautiful for many months afterwards: because the dust drifted round the world and took long to settle.

When we look through a slightly misty atmosphere at hills that are far away they seem to be blue: but of course they are not sending us blue light. The blue comes from the molecules and particles of the atmosphere which lie between them and us; a part of the sky fills the intervening space.

A cloud is an assemblage, generally, of drops which are large enough to scatter all the colours of the spectrum, and so when the clouds reflect the sun's rays to our eyes they are masses of shining white. When they lie between us and the sun they may intercept all the light and appear black; at the edges only enough light passes and is scattered to show the silver lining.

The Colour of the Sea

The blue colour of the deep sea is to be explained in a similar way. This has been a more difficult matter to prove, and even great observers like the late Lord Rayleigh were in doubt about it. Undoubtedly much of the blue of the sea is due to reflection from the sky: it might at first be supposed to be sufficiently explained in this way. We cannot but observe that under a blue sky the sea also looks blue, especially when a light wind chases ripples upon the surface, and the slopes of the ripples reflect to us the light from above. Under a leaden sky the sea looks grey.

Near the shore the water is green because there is fine sand in suspension which scatters the short waves, and when the sun shines through to the sand there is reflected yellow to be added to the scattered light. If there is seaweed the deep ruddy browns combine with the blue and green to make purples. Sometimes water, fresh or salt, contains so much suspended matter in a fine state of division, or so much air in the form of fine bubbles that even a small amount of water looks green. The glacier fed water of Lake Pukaki in New Zealand is green even in the bucket: and no doubt the phenomenon is not infrequent.

Thus there are examples in plenty which show how suspended matter can give blue to the sea: and yet it can be shown that the molecules of the water scatter a blue as do the molecules of the air. Lately, Sir C. V. Raman of Calcutta concluded from observations made during an ocean passage that the violet blue of the deep sea

PLATE XV

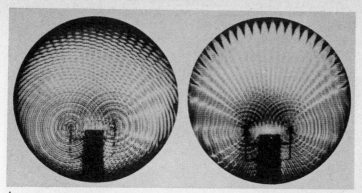

A. These two photographs are due to Professor Andrade. They represent the spread of ripples on a mercury surface. The ripples start from two points where dippers strike the surface at regular and frequent intervals. The photograph on the left is taken by an electric spark; that on the right by a flash lasting one second. Interference is easily seen: and the separation into radial tufts represents the genesis of diffracted beams, which are many in number because the dippers are wide apart. (*p.* 134)

B. The tube which Tyndall used in his experiments on the light scattered by fine particles suspended in the air. (*p.* 149)

C. Eriometers made and used by Young. In each of these is a fibre holder, a screen with small holes and a sliding scale. The mode of use is described on *p.* 162.

PLATE XVI

A. In this sketch the river water is clear, and the overhanging tree casts no shadow on the surface. (*p.* 153)

B. But in this sketch the water is muddy and shadows lie on it. Comparison of these two sketches should not be extended to consideration of the relative tones of the two as wholes. The muddy water is actually illuminated by the sun; but the point could not conveniently be brought out by a relative adjustment of the tones of two such simple sketches. (*p.* 153)

was to be explained in this way: and he made experiments in the laboratory which actually demonstrated the scattering from a ray of light passing through very pure water.

A ray of light striking the surface of smooth clear water is not scattered in all directions from the place where it strikes. The surface is not therefore visible; there are no details upon it to be distinguished. A tree overhanging clear water casts no shadow on the surface. There is, however, a shadow if the water is muddy and the suspended particles are sufficient to scatter the light before it has penetrated far, because in that case the eye can see a difference where the sunlight does not strike the water. Such a shadow is not to be confounded with the reflection of the tree: the former is on the surface, the latter is as far underneath as the tree is above. A cloud casts a shadow on a sparkling sea because it cuts off light which the ripples and waves reflect into our eyes: on a smooth sea we may see the reflection of the cloud in the water. If one looks over the side of a steamer at its shadow on the water, one sees that the shadow does not extend to those parts of the surface where the sea is pure and deep blue in colour. The shadow is visible only where the motion of the steamer has churned up the sea and filled it with air bubbles. There the walls of the bubbles turn the light aside into the eye, so that if the light is cut off by the steamer's bulk, the scattering ceases and there is a shadow.

On the water of a muddy river the shadow is strong and complete (Plate XVI).

Haloes

The haloes that at times surround the sun and moon are also scattering effects occurring under special circumstances. When suspended particles are very small, they scatter in all directions: and when they are large compared to the wave-length of light they reflect like solid objects or drops of water. There is a critical size between these two extremes which is the cause of the halo; viz., when drop and wave are approximately of the same dimensions. We had a parallel case when we observed the action of the diffraction grating, in which case the spacings of the grating were of the same order of size as the wave-length of light (see Fig. 66). It was only when this rough equality of dimensions was observed that the diffracted beams of the grating were observable. If the centres of the openings were too far apart they acted independently: if they were too close together the secondary wave-fronts of Fig. 66 could not be formed. It is so also when drops cause diffraction effects, the drops must neither be too big nor be too small.

It is easy to see that if a drop of water suspended in the atmosphere has any diffraction effect at all, that is to say, if it causes any separation of colours, it must make a halo because there is no other way in which the effect can be displayed. If light of a particular wave-length is specially scattered in some particular direction, which is the essential feature of diffraction, and if a screen is put to receive the scattered light, it must appear on the screen in the form of a ring of which the centre is C

(Fig. 72), which is the centre of the projection of the drop upon the screen. That is so because the particular direction spoken of may be disposed in any way about the line DC, so long as it always makes the same angle with DC. We might expect also that the less the wavelength the less the angle between the particular direction of scattering and the original direction, so that the halo

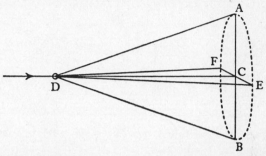

Fig. 72. If the diffracted ray from the drop D makes an angle equal to A D C with the original direction D C, then the diffracted rays as a whole will form a ring upon a screen, as in the figure, because all such directions as D A, D B, D E, D F make the same angle with D C.

due to a single drop must be coloured, the blue being on the inside of the ring. We can easily demonstrate the effect experimentally. Before doing so, however, we may consider the theory in rather more detail because in doing so we find further evidence of the power of the wave hypothesis.

We begin with picturing to ourselves an experiment which can actually be performed in the laboratory if due care is taken. Suppose that we make two small holes, whose centres are A and B, in a card SS (Fig. 73): and that we place the card before a point source of light as the figure indicates. We say a 'point' source, because a broad source would give so many over-lapping pictures that the effect to be observed would be blurred. On the further side of the screen, two sets of spherical waves diverge from A and B and eventually strike the screen SS. At some points on the screen the two sets are in phase when they strike and add their effects together. At others they interfere and there is

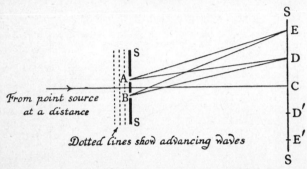

Fig. 73. Two small openings in a screen admit waves of light from the left. At c the two sets of spherical waves that open out from A and B reinforce one another and there is light. If D B is longer than D A by half a wave-length there is no light at D because the two sets of waves interfere on Young's principle. There is light again at E, when E B is longer than E A by a whole wave-length, and the two sets of waves are again in the same phase. Other lines of light and darkness occur alternately. The positions of the lines depend on the wave-length, for blue they are closer together than for red.

darkness. For instance, at C, a point on the screen in the plane of the diagram and equidistant from A and B, the wave systems add together and there is light. This applies not only to C, which lies in the plane of the paper, but to all points on the screen which are equi-distant from A and B whether they lie in the plane of the diagram or not. There is, in fact, a line of light as indicated in the next figure by the horizontal straight line through C; this figure shows the appearance on the screen regarded from the front.

At a point D on the screen, such that DA is longer than DB by half a wave-length, the two sets of waves continuously oppose one another, and there is darkness. This applies also to points lying on a line, as shown in Fig. 74: the line is slightly curved because at points to the right and left of D the distances from A and B are greater than at D, and the point where the one distance

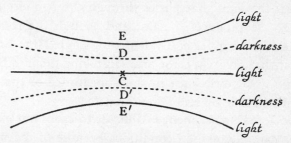

Fig. 74. The screen s s, of Fig. 73, is looked at from the front. Light appears along the firm lines, shadows along the dotted lines. There is a succession of such lines, of which only a few are drawn. Each is a narrow spectrum.

is half a wave length greater than the other is a little further away from the horizontal line through C. Thus there are formed upon the screen sets of bright lines.

The process involves a separation of colour because the position of points such as D and E and of the lines that go through them depend upon the wave length. Thus the blue lines lie closer to the horizontal line of Fig. 74 than the red: in fact the lines form a set of spectra.

Suppose now that we spin the card containing the two holes A and B about an axis which is perpendicular to the card and passes through the middle point between A and B. The figure on the screen will rotate simultaneously. The two holes become a ring, or, if they originally touched, which they might have done, a large circle. The figure on the screen becomes a halo with C as centre and a radius rather larger than CE. It is easy to demonstrate this last point by drawing two black lines on a card to represent the bright curves through E and E', and then rotating this card in its own plane about C as centre. If the lines of the drawing are coloured, the halo is imitated still more closely.

Thus the light that passes through the two circles as they rotate produces a halo: and though the rotating circles are not quite equivalent to a single large hole it is clear that no great error arises in taking them to be so, and no great difference in the appearance of the halo would be made by rectifying the defect.

The actual experiment is difficult to carry out except under carefully chosen conditions because of the smallness of some of its dimensions. If the centres of the holes A and B were half a millimetre apart, and the screen were a metre away the radius of the halo would be about two millimetres: also it would be very feeble as well as small.

We have one more step to make before we complete our explanation. For it will be observed that we have been showing how a halo can result from the passage of light through a small hole: whereas we want to see the consequence of its passage round a small obstacle. But the one can be shown to be the equivalent of the other, the same halo follows from either of the two arrangements. That this should be so is a simple but very interesting consequence of the wave theory to which attention was drawn by Babinet in 1837: his argument was as follows:—

Suppose that the screen SS were made of glass. If the glass were clear everywhere there would be no halo. If it were blackened all over except for a small hole, the halo would be formed. Now, the case of the glass when all clear can be looked on as the joint effect of two other cases: the first all black except for the hole, and the second all clear except for a black spot occupying the position of the hole. The joint effect of the last two is the same as that of the first, the 'all clear,' which we know to have no effect at a point such as E. The last two must therefore so mutually interfere that they destroy each other. A wave motion can only be destroyed by an equal wave motion which has the same wave-length, but is so adjusted that the crest of one fits the hollow of the other, and vice versâ. Thus the last case, viz., the black spot on the clear screen must also produce a halo of the same character as the small hole in the black screen. The difference between the two which causes mutual destruction when they are superimposed is not one which our eyes can detect: the one system of waves is merely shifted forwards or backwards with respect to the other by half a wave-length.

We can now proceed to actual experiment. To make a halo of convenient size for observation the particle must be very small indeed, something like a tenth to a fiftieth of a millimetre in diameter. The halo due to one such particle would be too weak to be seen. But we may easily combine the effect of thousands of such particles. If we place a glass screen in front of a fine pencil of light and breathe upon it, the minute drops that settle upon the glass will add their haloes together especially if they are all of approximately the same size. For, although the particles occupy different positions, their diffuse haloes are practically superimposed on one another. The combination gives us a visible effect (Fig. 75). A clean piece of glass left face upwards in a quiet room for some time gathers enough fine dust to show haloes: but if we breathe upon the glass the number of drops is so

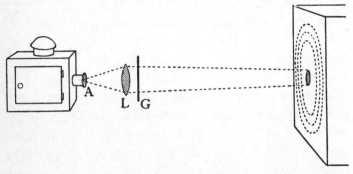

Fig. 75. Light from the lantern issues through a small opening at A and is focused by the lens L upon a hole in the side of the box shown on the right of the diagram. Passing through the hole into the box, which is blackened inside, it is lost to view. The glass sheet G covered with fine dust or drops of moisture causes the halo which appears on the side of the box: the disappearance of the main beam allows the relatively faint halo to be easily visible.

large that the effect is much enhanced. At first the drops are very small, and it is curious to see how the rings due to the dust that is already there are reinforced by other rings which spread over the screen and then contract rapidly as the very small drops evaporate and coalesce. All colours are found in the rings, and in a dark room the effect is beautiful. It is usual, in arranging the experiment, to provide a hole in the centre of the screen through which the main ray of light passes and is lost to view: otherwise the dazzle which is due to its striking the white screen obscures the delicate colours.

The halo round the moon or sun is due to similar causes, but it must be observed that the eye does not receive the different colours from the same drop (Fig. 76). Suppose M is the moon and E the eye. A drop suspended in the atmosphere at D would, as in the experiment just

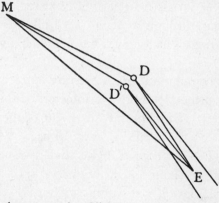

Fig. 76.   The drop at D sends red light to the eye, and the drop at D′ sends blue.   Hence a coloured halo round the moon, which is seen in the direction E M.

described, produce a halo on an intercepting screen of which the centre would be where MD met the screen. The eye is, let us say, in the outer part of the halo where it receives red from D. It does not receive blue from the same drop because the blue ring is inside the red and does not fall on the eye. But a drop at D′ produces a halo from which the eye may receive blue. Thus the eye receives red from D and blue from D′, and as the effect is symmetrical about the line ME which joins the moon to the eye, the observer sees a halo round the moon, blue inside and red out. The result resembles exactly that which in our experiment appeared upon the screen: there is only the slight difference in the manner of formation. For a good halo the drops should be of uniform size, so that the separate haloes are superimposed and add their effects. The larger the halo is, the smaller are water drops that produce it.

It is easy to reproduce the experiment for the individual observer. It is necessary only to look at a bright point of light through a plane piece of glass on which a thin covering of little drops has been deposited by the breath.

Thomas Young made an interesting application of the diffraction principle in his 'eriometer,' an instrument which he devised for the measurement of the diameters of wool fibres. It is still in practical use. When a fine fibre is held in a beam of light, and transverse to the direction of the beam, bright lines appear on a screen on which the shadow is cast, running alongside the shadow on either side. The explanation is similar to that which has already been used for the case of the two small holes, and it is unnecessary to go into it. If a number of fibres pointing in all directions which are perpendicular to the ray of light are placed in the path of the ray, the various pairs of lines will lie criss-cross on the screen: and if there are enough of them the effect will be the same as if a single strong pair had been spun round, as in a previous reference to Fig. 74. That is to say there will be a halo, and the diameter of the halo depends on the fineness of the fibre.

The instrument is illustrated in Plate XVc where the eye looks through a mass of fibre mounted on a pin at a small bright spot: the latter being due to a light or bright surface behind a screen in which is a small hole. The bright spot is seen to be surrounded by a ring.

Diffraction effects may be continually observed. The street lamps at night show a coloured star when looked at through the top of one's umbrella. The arms of the star are parallel to the warp and weft of the umbrella material. Or one may see the same effect through a silk curtain, or through any fine and not too opaque woven material. The children look at the bright fire through half closed eyes and see, as they say, straws coming out of the flames. A glass pane wiped with a greasy cloth leaves furrows in parallel rows which show red and green coloration.

A diffraction effect always produces colour by separation of wave-lengths, and in this it is distinct from the result of a pigment which is due to a selective destruction of colour. It can be shown, as the above examples will illustrate, to be the natural and special consequence of a wave theory. During the hundred years after Young diffraction was studied in a great variety of its forms, and the perfect satisfaction which it gave in the explanation of observed results and the prediction of others as yet unknown was, and is, a chief support of the wave theory. It must be true as far as it goes.

CHAPTER VI

THE POLARISATION OF LIGHT

The Qualities of Light

THERE is a certain quality of light which the eye cannot observe or measure. Direction, intensity, colour can all be observed and are used in the process of vision: these qualities or their analogues are common to all kinds of waves, ether waves, water waves, and the air waves of sound. The additional quality differentiates between various forms of wave. It has reference to the mode of motion within the wave itself; not the forward motion of the wave system, but the motion in the medium through which the wave is passing.

For example, when waves travel over the surface of the sea, the water at any one spot rises and falls as the waves pass by. It is only the form of the wave that travels forward, not its substance. A ship, or other object floating on the surface is not carried forward by the wave: it merely rises and falls, swaying a little forwards and backwards. A swimmer lying on his back in the open sea is heaved up and down as the waves pass under him, but they do not carry him along. Only near the shore where the motion takes a different character, and is not strictly a wave, but a 'breaker,' is the water hurled up the beach and the swimmer with it. The sea-wave is a 'transverse wave,' the motions of the water

164

being transverse to the direction in which the wave system is travelling.

The motion of the air in a sound wave is quite different. The air molecules move backwards and forwards in the line of motion of the system, and not from side to side. Tyndall, in his Christmas Lectures placed a row of boys in front of the lecture table, each boy with his hands on the shoulders of the boy in front. He gave a shove to the boy at one end of the row, whereupon the shove, like a pulse, ran along the line and the boy at the other end fell on to a mattress prepared for him. All motions were along the line. If, with less violent action, he had rocked the last boy backwards and forwards, the successive impulses would have travelled along the line as a system of waves, and would have represented in greater detail the passage of a sound wave through the air or any material substance. The molecules of the air correspond to the boys: their to and fro motions being, of course, incomparably quicker than were realised in Tyndall's experiment.

Lastly we may think of a flick given to a rope, of which one end is held in the hand while the other is fixed. A pulse runs along the rope, and this resembles the movements of a light wave more closely than either of the preceding cases. It is a transverse wave, like a wave on the sea, not a 'longitudinal' wave like that of sound. But the sea wave is limited as to the directions in which water movements take place; the water rises and falls, but does not move at all from side to side horizontally in a direction perpendicular to that of travel. The rope supplies a more complete analogy: the transverse movements may take place in any direction perpendicular to the rope. And this is what must be supposed to be possible in the case of light, in order to account for certain phenomena.

The importance of the hypothesis lies in the opportunity which it affords of endowing light with a new quality which is not indeed perceived by the eye, but can be detected in other ways, and must somehow be accounted for. As we shall see, it is usually detected by the use of crystals of certain kinds: it may then be observed on a great scale in the light from the sky, and in reflection from the surfaces of transparent bodies like the sea.

As this question is of great interest and importance, and its examination by a succession of workers has contributed greatly to our present ideas of light, and as its history illustrates beautifully the gradual growth of a scientific idea, let us consider it from its beginnings in the time of Newton and Huygens. 'There is brought from Iceland, which is an Island in the North Sea, in the latitude of 66 degrees,' writes Christiaan Huygens in 1678, 'a kind of Crystal or transparent stone, very remarkable for its figure and other qualities but above all for its strange refractions.' We know now that most crystals have similar properties, but doubtless the 'stone from Iceland' was notable on account of its size and clearness and of the magnitude of the phenomenon. Huygens says that Erasmus Bartolimus first drew attention to the crystal, but he writes his own treatise[1] nevertheless, 'for I have applied myself with great exactitude to

[1] Huygens's *Treatise on Light.* Translated by Silvanus P. Thompson (Macmillan).

examine these properties of refraction in order to be quite
sure before undertaking to explain the causes of them.'
Photographs of pieces of Iceland Spar are shown in

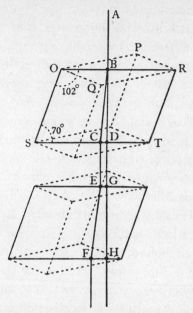

Fig. 77. The figure is redrawn from that which Huygens gives in his
Treatise. For convenience of representation the crystal is supposed to be
cut so that O P, O Q and O S are all equal, in which case O T is the axis through
O, and O R T S is a section containing the axis. The ray A B is perpendicular
to the face O P R Q; it divides into the ordinary ray B D, which is in line with
A B, and B C which is not: both rays lie in the plane O R T S. On leaving the
crystal they resume their original direction.

Plates XVII, XVIII. We now know that its composition
is $CaCO_3$, calcium carbonate. The spar cleaves easily
along certain planes so that it takes naturally the form
of a rhomb. This is to be seen in Plate XVIIA, most
clearly in the case of the separate piece lying on the
table below the larger pieces used in the optical experiment: also in the photograph of Plate XVIIIA. At two

corners of the rhomb (Fig. 77) O and T the angles of the faces are all obtuse, being 102° nearly.

The point which first attracted the interest of Huygens was the curious division of every ray (special cases excepted) which entered the crystal, into two rays proceeding in different directions through the crystal; though they resumed their original directions on emerging they were still distinct from one another and pursued different, but parallel, paths. Fig. 77, which is copied from Huygens's *Treatise*, will make the effect clear. The ray AB is supposed – for the sake of simplicity – to strike the crystal at right angles to the surface. It then divides into two rays BC and BD which on emergence become the parallel rays CE and DG. The illustration in Plate XVIIA shows the effect clearly. In this arrangement a ray of light is directed upon a piece of spar: its path in the air before it strikes the spar is made visible by the aid of a little smoke. Inside the spar the double track is invisible because the crystal is so clear that there is very little to scatter the rays. But on leaving the crystal again the two portions become visible in the smoky air.

This separation of one ray into two can also be made evident by laying a piece of spar upon a sheet of paper on which there is a black dot or mark of any kind: the dot then appears double. In Plate XVIIIA is shown the doubling of a line of print.

If now we try this experiment for various positions of the spar in relation to the incident light we find, as Huygens did when he undertook the examination of the problem, that the two portions into which the ray divides

differ in their behaviour. One of them follows the
ordinary rules of refraction. For instance if we lay the
spar upon a paper on which there is a single black dot
and turn the spar round, keeping it in contact with the
paper, one of the images remains at rest: just as would
be the case were a piece of glass substituted for the spar

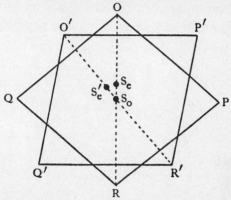

Fig. 78. This diagram shows the relation between the ordinary and extraordinary images of a black spot seen through the crystal of Iceland spar.
The observer sees black spots at S_0 and S_e of which the former is the nearer.
If the crystal is turned round, to O' P' R' Q' for example, the spot S_0 does not
move, but S_e moves to $S'e$; which latter point lies on O' R'.
If the crystal is moved about on the paper without rotation, neither spot
moves.

(Fig. 78). The other revolves in a circle about the
first, and its position is clearly connected with the form
and position of the crystal. The line joining the two
images is parallel to the bisector of the larger angle of
the face. The one that stays still seems much nearer
than the other. Clearly its refraction is greater: the
light that makes it must travel more slowly in the
crystal than that which makes the other.

The ray that obeys the ordinary rules is called the
ordinary ray, and the other the extraordinary. Huygens

set himself to find out the rules which governed the direction of the extraordinary ray. In this he was completely successful: his *Treatise* describes the ingenious methods by which he obtained his solution. He was not able, however, to explain the physical behaviour of these rays, nor to connect them with the nature of the crystal: his account of his failure is as interesting as that of his geometrical successes, as we shall now see.

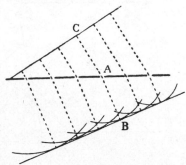

Fig. 79. A set of waves passing through apertures in a screen into a medium where its velocity is less than before. Circular ripples are shown forming one of the wave fronts.

His earlier work on the reflection and refraction of waves at surfaces separating air from glass or water, or, in general, one transparent body from another, had led him to employ a certain geometrical construction, which in effect we have already employed ourselves.

Suppose that an advancing wave meets a screen pierced with a number of apertures. In the experiment of Fig. 66 the wave front is parallel to the screen, but we will remove this restriction and imagine the approach to be made obliquely as in Fig. 79. Each opening becomes in its turn a source from which circular ripples spread on the other side of the screen. These gradually merge into one wave front, as we have seen before. If the velocity on both sides of the screen is the same, the new wave front is parallel to the old. If the velocities are different the inclination of the front is altered (Fig. 79, also Figs. 20 and 21). Now it cannot make any difference if the apertures are altered either in number or size. There might be a very large number all close together: indeed, there need be no screen at all.

We should note one further point before we proceed. The ripple from A in our experiment is shown as having reached the point B where it contributes its quota to the wave front. If A were blocked there would be a deficiency of disturbances at B; in the optical analogy there would be a deficiency of light. If the screen were merely figurative, defining a boundary between two transparent media, an obstruction at A would cast a shadow at B. We may therefore say that AB is the direction of the ray of light after refraction. The direction before refraction was CA. This was how Huygens analysed the phenomenon of refraction.

If a similar mode of explanation was to be successful in the case of the crystal, some extension or modification was necessary. The extraordinary ray could not be due merely to the existence of a second light velocity in the crystal, to be represented by a second set of spherical waves. Two velocities would make two rays it was true, but both should follow the ordinary laws of refraction whereas the extraordinary ray followed rules of its own, which brought in the disposition of the crystal to the incident ray.

Huygens saw therefore that the rules of the extraordinary ray could not be referred to spherical waves;
and he tried 'what Elliptical waves or rather spheroidal
waves, would do.' They proved to be sufficient for the
solution of his problem. It was entirely natural that he
should try the spheroid since it was the next simplest
surface to the sphere, which had been ruled out as too
simple. The spheroid, of which the earth supplies a
well known example, is formed by the revolution of an
ellipse about one of its axes, which becomes the axis of
the spheroid. His waves were to spread in spheroidal
surfaces. Huygens found that they must be of the
oblate kind, as in the case of the earth; of which the
polar diameter or axis is the minimum diameter.

These spheroidal surfaces must obviously be related
to the form of the crystal, which means that the axis
of the spheroid must be connected with the lines of the
rhomb. The conception of the spheroidal surface would
be meaningless otherwise. At once there comes into
view an explanation of the observed fact (Fig. 77) that
the extraordinary ray follows a direction which is connected with the crystal form.

If this is so, there is only one possible direction which
the spheroidal axis can take: it must coincide with the
direction of the axis of the crystal. This is the direction
of that line through O (Fig. 77) where the three angles
are all 102°, which is equally inclined to the three faces
meeting in O. It may be well to remind ourselves
that an axis in a crystal is not a particular line, but a
particular direction. An axis may be drawn through
any point. In Fig. 77 the axis drawn through O does

not go through the opposite corner of the rhomb unless
PO, OQ, and OS are all equal: which is merely a matter
of the way in which the spar is cut.   The position of the
axis refers to the properties of the crystal and not to its
dimensions.

Now let us see how Huygens used his new conception

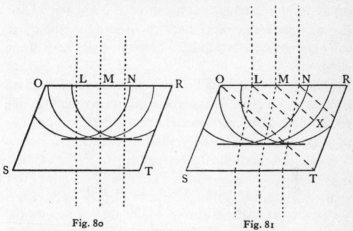

Fig. 80   Fig. 81

The two figures 80 and 81 illustrate Huygens's construction for the ordinary and extraordinary rays in Iceland spar.

for the explanation of his observations.   Take the case
represented in Fig. 77 where the ray AB represents a
series of waves advancing upon the crystal, their front
being parallel to the crystal face.   A wave-front (Figs. 80
and 81) strikes the face of the crystal, and its further progress is to be calculated, according to the Huygens
method, by drawing wave surfaces spreading away from
various points of incidence L M N.   The figure for the
case where the ordinary laws of refraction are followed
shows the wave surfaces spherical, as on previous occasions and the dotted lines show the progress of the ray.

The ordinary ray behaves as if the crystal were like glass. But for the extraordinary ray the wave surfaces are spheroids with axes parallel to the axis of the crystal. These spheroids in Fig. 81 replace the spheres of Fig. 80: it is now seen that the wave-front in the crystal moves obliquely and thus the experimental observations are accounted for. Huygens measured the amount of the deviation of the extraordinary ray from the ordinary in this case and was thus able to determine the form of the spheroid.

This extension of his methods was found to account completely for every experimental observation of the geometrical relations between the incident ray and the two rays into which the crystal divided it. It was a remarkable achievement.

The 'Surprising Phenomenon' of Huygens

Further than this Huygens could not go because the existence and nature of the quality which we call polarisation were not realised by him. His difficulties are best set out in his own words. He describes as follows a 'surprising phenomenon touching the rays which pass through two separated pieces; the cause of which is not explained.' The figure which he drew to illustrate his observations is reproduced in Fig. 77, and his description is as follows (the photographs of Plate XVIIA, B, C show the actual effects):—

'The phenomenon is, that by taking two pieces of this crystal and applying them one over the other, or rather holding them with a space between the two, if all the sides of one are parallel to those of the other then a ray of light such as AB, is divided into two in the first piece namely into BD and BC, following the two refractions regular and irregular. On penetrating thence into the other piece each ray will pass there without further dividing itself into two: but that one which underwent the regular refraction as here DG will undergo again only a regular refraction at GH: and the other, CE, an irregular refraction at EF. . . . Now it is marvellous why the rays CE and DG, incident from the air on the lower crystal do not divide themselves the same as the first ray AB. One would say that it must be that the ray DG in passing through the upper piece has lost something which is necessary to move the matter which serves for the irregular refraction: and that likewise CE has lost that which was necessary to move the matter which serves for regular refraction. . . .' That is to say, one must expect an ordinary ray to be always an ordinary ray, and an extraordinary to be always an extraordinary. He goes on 'but there is yet another thing which upsets this reasoning. It is that when one disposes the two crystals in such a way that the planes which constitute the principal sections intersect each other at right angles . . . then the ray which has come by the regular refraction, as DG, undergoes only an irregular refraction in the lower piece, and on the contrary the ray which has come by the irregular refraction, as CE, undergoes only a regular refraction. . . .' That is to say, the ordinary ray has become the extraordinary, and vice versâ. A principal section is one that passes through one of the edges that meet at the obtuse corner (Fig. 77) and bisects the angle between the other two edges, for example OSTR in Fig. 77.

'But in all the infinite other positions, besides those which I have just stated' (viz. that for which the principal sections are parallel and that for which they are perpendicular), 'the rays DG and CE divide themselves anew each one into two, by refraction in the lower crystal, so that from the single ray AB there are four, sometimes of equal brightness, sometimes some much less bright than others, according to the varying agreement in the positions of the crystals: but they do not appear to have all together more light than the single ray AB.

'When one considers here how, while the rays CE, DG, remain the same, it depends on the position that one gives to the lower piece, whether it divides them both in two or whether it does not divide them, and yet how the ray AB above is always divided, it seems that one is obliged to conclude that the waves of light, after having passed through the first crystal, acquire a certain form or disposition in virtue of which, when meeting the texture of the second crystal, in certain positions, they can move the two different kinds of matter which serve for the two species of refraction; and when meeting the second crystal in another position are able to move only one of these kinds of matter.   But to tell how this occurs, I have hitherto found nothing which satisfies me.'   So he 'leaves to others this research.'   He could not guess what his 'certain form or disposition' might be: the ray of light after leaving the first crystal had acquired 'sides' to use the term current for long afterwards.   His reference to the 'two different kinds of matter' is in consonance with his own way of explaining the double refraction and need not trouble us now.

176

PLATE XVII

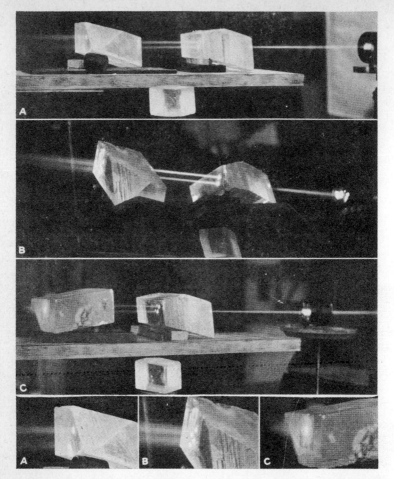

A. Two blocks of Iceland Spar are placed in parallel positions. They are large blocks in the possession of the Royal Institution which have not been cut to form regular rhombs, but the natural edges are easily seen to be parallel. The single ray from the lantern, made visible by diffusing smoke through the air is doubled by the first prism, and the separation is again increased by the second. Observe that the white spots which mark the points of emergence are on a line which is parallel to the bisector of the obtuse angle of the face on which they lie. (*pp.* 167, 174, 177)

B. Here the second block is turned round, the faces where the rays emerge being kept parallel in the two crystals. The two rays from the first are now further subdivided. There are four spots on the face of emergence from the second block. (*pp.* 174, 177)

C. The second block has now been turned round by 180° from its position in VI.A. It happens that the two blocks are of nearly equal thickness and the two rays that emerge from the first block are reunited when they leave the second. (*pp.* 174, 177) The faces of emergence are shown on a larger scale in additional photographs, in order that the spots may be seen more clearly.

The observations of Huygens are illustrated by the photographs (Plate XVII). The ray of light in Plate XVIIA is divided into two by its passage through the block of Iceland spar on the right of the picture, the tracks before and after being made visible by scattering from the smoke which has been blown into the air. A second block of spar is set so that its edges are parallel to those of the first. The orientations of the two blocks are identical; in other words their positions are similar. In this case there is no further division of the rays; the passage through the second block merely causes a wider separation of the two paths already existing. The rays can be followed by observing either their tracks in the air or the bright spots, due to scattering at unpolished surfaces, where they enter and leave the blocks. It may be observed that the line joining the blocks is parallel to the bisector of the obtuse angle of the faces through which they pass in agreement with the indications of previous figures.

In Plate XVIIB the second block has been turned round, the axis of the movement being the direction of the rays. There are now four rays after the passage through the second block. The point of view has been altered so that the further subdivision may be clearer. This is one of the 'infinite other positions' of Huygens.

In Plate XVIIc the second block has been turned through two right angles; and now, it will be observed, the two rays that emerge from the first block are re-united after passage through the second. The two pieces of spar happen to be very nearly of the same thickness, and their actions compensate each other.

The Experiment of Malus

A century passed with no further attempt at an explanation of the mystery. But in 1808 Malus happened to be looking through a piece of Iceland spar at the light of the setting sun reflected in the windows of the Luxemburg Palace in Paris, and was surprised to find that the two images were not of equal intensity. On turning round the spar which he held in his hand, just as one of the pieces of spar is turned in Fig. 78, an operation which he would quite naturally perform because of the fascination of seeing the two images revolve round each other, he observed that they grew and diminished in intensity. This is just what happened in Huygens's experiment Fig. 78: Malus had thus found that light reflected from a piece of glass also had 'sides.' He invented the term 'polarisation' to describe the condition of such a ray, implying that there was the same sort of difference – as one looks along the ray – as exists between various directions that may be drawn on a compass card: a line joining N and S poles differs from a line joining E and W, or any other direction. It was not a very good choice of words because 'polarity' is rather the property of direction accompanied by difference at the two ends; it applies to an arrow, but not to a curtain rod.

It is easy to repeat the experiment (Plate XVIIIᴮ). In the photograph the block of Iceland spar is so placed that the ordinary and extraordinary rays lie in the same vertical plane. A piece of glass is placed so that any reflections lie in the same plane. It will be observed that the ordinary ray is reflected and the extraordinary ray is not. The rays have 'sides.'

This was at the time when Young was developing his principle of the interference of waves, and was trying to rehabilitate the wave theory which had long been under a cloud. The philosophers of that time were firm adherents of a corpuscular theory of light based on Newton's work, and Young met with great opposition. The discovery which Malus had made intensified his difficulties: for he could not suggest any way in which the wave theory, as he imagined it, could have 'sides.' That was because he had not grasped all the possibilities of the theory. He assumed that the vibrations were like those of sound, and took place in the line of advance of the wave system. His picture of the process was based on the supposed behaviour of bodies like steel or glass or water in the manner of Tyndall's experiment with the row of boys. Such movements have nothing of a side to side character. It was a long time before Young saw that the difficulty could be overcome by the assumption that light waves were of the transverse kind. This may seem curious when one reflects that the waves on the surface of the sea are transverse waves; but it may be suggested that the very fact of these waves being confined to the surface would prevent their being thought of as illustrating the passage of a wave motion through the body of the water. Many must have felt or be feeling the same difficulty. It is one of the continually recurring consequences of the use of analogies.

The Transverse Vibrations of Young and Fresnel

Eventually Young found the way of escape. In January 1817, nine years after Malus made his discovery, he wrote to Arago: 'I have also been reflecting on the possibility of giving an imperfect explanation of the affection of light which constitutes polarisation, without departing from the genuine doctrine of undulation.' He suggested the possibility of a 'transverse vibration propagated in the direction of the radius, the motions of the particles being in a certain constant direction with respect to that radius: and this,' he added, 'is polarisation.' He had not thought at the time of this writing that the motions of the particles might be at right angles only, and not in various oblique directions to the ray of light. But he had made a very great step forwards. The brilliant young French engineer, Fresnel, grasped the significance of this suggestion and proceeded to show that it could be made the basis of a theory which would cover all the phenomena of the movements of light within a crystal, including the separation into two rays as well as the polarisation. Fresnel had at that time actually worked out for himself the theory of the interference of light, not knowing that Young had already accomplished the task in England: but he at once acknowledged that he had been anticipated and defended Young's position enthusiastically. He wrote Young in 1816: 'But if anything could console me for not having the advantage of priority, it was for me to have met a savant who has enriched physics with so great a number of important discoveries, and has at the same time contributed greatly to strengthen my confidence in the theory I have adopted.' Young replied in terms equally courteous. The dominant position of the wave theory during the nineteenth century was certainly due, in the first place, to the combined labours of these two men.

As soon as the transverse character of the wave of light was established all went well with the further development of the wave theory, until the end of the century. It was strong enough to bear extension in a great number of directions, and the writers and experimenters found that they could rely upon it to explain very intricate phenomena.

The consideration of all these developments would carry us far away from our main purpose, which is a sketch in broad outline of the part that light plays in the universe. And of course, many of them cannot be investigated without mathematical calculation, and reference to other theories, particularly those of electricity and magnetism. We may however return to the observation of Huygens and see how the conception of a transverse polarisation resolves his difficulties. And at the same time we may see how the whole matter is bound up with the ideas of crystal structure which in recent years have been developed so largely. First of all let us restate our definition of the terms which we use. In a *polarised* ray the movements or vibrations are all parallel to one direction, which is of course perpendicular to the ray. A wave motion on the sea can be said to be polarised because all the motions are vertical and perpendicular to the horizontal direction in which the waves are moving. It is not necessary to form a mental picture of what it is that moves in the ray of light: it is sufficient to conceive a wave motion with its attendant phenomena of interference and the rest.

An unpolarised or normal ray has no special direction of movement, except that all movements are transverse to the direction of the ray. Most light rays are nearly free of polarisation, though some amount of it is of frequent occurrence because reflection is apt to produce it. It will be remembered that the eye cannot tell whether a ray is unpolarised or partly or wholly polarised.

Let us suppose now that a normal or unpolarised ray breaks up on entering a crystal into two rays of equal strength which are each completely polarised: and that the vibrations in the two are at right angles to each other. This will satisfy our experiments. In Plate XVIIA for example, the primary ray contained transverse vibrations of every orientation, but the two rays issuing from the first block are to be considered as polarised. On entering the second block the vibrations of the ordinary ray (the lower one in the figure, continuing the primary) are in such a direction that there is no further subdivision. The ordinary ray of the one continues as the ordinary ray of the other: all its vibrations are already in the right direction for this to happen. So also the extraordinary ray continues as the extraordinary. But when the second block is placed as in Plate XVIIB the vibrations of each of the two rays that leave the first block are in such a direction that they cannot pass through the second block in the manner of either an ordinary or an extraordinary ray. Each has to be further subdivided. In Plate XVIIc the ordinary ray of the first block becomes the extraordinary of the second, and vice versâ. The action of the first is reversed by the second. If this hypothesis is correct, the effects must be due in some way to crystal structure. What is there in crystal structure which can be the cause of them?

Polarisation due to Crystal Structure

The fundamental fact is the existence of atomic arrangement in the crystal, which is thereby endowed with all its characteristic properties. And we may observe that these properties are of universal occurrence because all solid substances tend to be crystalline and are in fact much further on the way to that condition than is obvious to the eye. The X-rays have greatly extended our knowledge in this respect. The atoms and molecules of which the crystal is built are disposed in regular array according to some definite pattern which is characteristic of the crystal. There is the same kind of difference between a crystal and a piece of glass as between a woven fabric or a block of wood on the one hand and a piece of unstretched indiarubber on the other. Various properties of the wood depend on direction: such as heat conductivity, resistance to crushing or tensions, contraction during seasoning and the like.

In the crystal the arrangement is on a far finer scale and cannot be perceived by the eye; atoms and molecules are too small to be seen. That the arrangement is regular has long been inferred on the ground that the external form of the crystal is so perfect and characteristic; the X-rays have now given us the power of discovering the pattern and placing therein the atoms in their relative positions. Some patterns are very simple, such as rocksalt or diamond. Such are, in fact, so

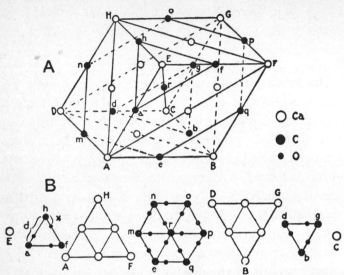

Fig. 82. The figure A represents the arrangement of the atoms of which Iceland spar, CaCO3 is composed. The clear white circles represent atoms of calcium, and the black circles represent carbon. The oxygen atoms are not shown in this figure, in order to avoid confusion. The arrangement of the atoms in successive layers, perpendicular to the principal axis E C are shown in the figure B. The oxygens are represented here by small black circles. The figures show the relative positions of the atoms and no more. The distance between the successive layers of B is 2.79 Angström units, about the hundred millionth part of an inch. The sizes and shapes of the atoms are not indicated in the figure, being far less easily determined than the relative positions of the centres of the atoms.

simple that the effects we are now linking up with structure are not manifested by them: a certain complexity is required for their production. In Iceland spar the complexity is sufficient and is such as to have a large effect. These circumstances and the perfect form of crystals which can be obtained of a considerable size, are the causes of the attention that has been given to the spar.

In Fig. 82 is shown the model of Iceland spar, giving the position of the atoms as the X-rays have placed them. As in every crystal there is a fundamental unit, and the model is sufficiently large to include a few repetitions of it or of portions of it. In each unit there are one atom of calcium, one of carbon, and three of oxygen. The model has clearly the same form as the spar of Fig. 77: this we must expect, for in fact the spar itself is merely a sufficient repetition of the fundamental unit. In the figure is shown, in addition to the model as a whole, various sections of it, in a series of drawings marked B. These sections are cut perpendicularly to the line EC, and show the atoms arranged in alternate layers, first a calcium layer, then one containing only CO_3 groups, that is to say, carbons each with three oxygens arranged symmetrically round them and so on. The CO_3 group is most clearly seen at r in the picture of the middle layer. In the second and sixth sections it only appears in part. If we cut out of the crystal a plate lying parallel to these planes and perpendicular to EC, such a plate possesses a certain symmetry: it is like that of a wire netting with a hexagonal mesh. The direction EC is known as the axis of the crystal because there is this symmetry about it. If we make physical experiment with such a plate the symmetry manifests itself at once. For example, the crystallographer Senarmont made measurements many years ago on the heat-conductivity of quartz, in the manner shown in Plate XVIIIc. Quartz, like Iceland spar, belongs to the class of crystals which possess a single axis of symmetry: many of their physical properties are therefore similar. He cut a plate of quartz perpendicular to the axis and drilled a hole through its centre. The plate was then coated with a thin layer of white wax. A wire passing through the hole was heated by an electric current and the wax began to melt. Senarmont found that the melted portion was circular in outline showing that the heat had spread equally in all directions from the wire. If, however, he cut the plate so that it was not perpendicular to the axis the outline of the melting was no longer circular. It was an oval as in the figure. The greatest departure from the circular form occurred when the plane of the plate included the axis. In fact, the experiment showed that conductivity was greatest along the axis and least in any direction perpendicular to it. In any other direction the conductivity lay between the two extremes.

Even in the complicated arrangement of the atoms in Iceland spar we can see how much less symmetry exists in a plane containing the axis than in a plane which is perpendicular thereto. The arrangement of the calcium and carbon atoms in a plane containing the axis is shown in Fig. 83. There is none of the symmetry shown by the hexagonal arrangement of Fig. 82.

Thus the peculiar structure of Iceland spar – and indeed of the majority of crystals – causes physical properties and happenings to depend on the direction in which they take place within the crystal. We have taken the spread of heat as our example. Now when light passes through a substance, the essential process is a vibration which, though we refer it to the ether, is somehow affected by the matter of the substance. We may well expect therefore that when light is going through a crystal the rate of travel will depend on the relation between the direction of the vibration and the characteristic directions of the crystal structure. All vibrations perpendicular to the axis of the crystal must be similar in character, as in the analogous case of the spreading of heat. Consequently all rays in which the vibration is perpendicular to the axis travel at the same

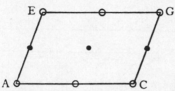

Fig. 83. The figure shows the arrangement of the atoms of the spar in the plane E A C G (Fig. 82). This corresponds to the plane O S T R of Fig. 77.

rate. These are in fact what Huygens called the ordinary rays. All others travel at different rates and form extraordinary rays.

But when a ray enters a crystal its vibrations are initially in all directions perpendicular to itself. Why then should a sorting take place, so that in the crystal there are only two directions of vibration, one of them perpendicular to the axis and forming the ordinary ray, and the other the extraordinary ray?

The answer to this question is common to many other instances of subdivision of energies of vibration. The vibrations of a steel rod will serve as an example. Suppose first of all that the rod is circular in section. If it is held loosely at the centre and struck at one end it bends to and fro at a certain rate and gives out the corresponding note. It does not matter where it is struck. But if the section is slightly elliptical the effect is less simple. The rod bends more easily one way than the other. If it is struck on the flat side of the ellipse at P (Fig. 84) it vibrates more slowly than if the stroke is given in the perpendicular direction at Q; the note is lower in pitch in the former case than in the latter. Suppose now that it is struck at R. It does not give out

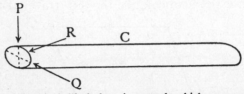

Fig. 84. A steel rod of elliptical section sounds a higher note when struck at Q than at P, the latter being on the flatter side. When struck at R, it emits both the high note of Q and the low note of P, but not a note of intermediate pitch.

a note intermediate between those due to strokes at P and Q, but a mixture of these two. This is the important point. The energy of vibration imparted by the stroke at R divides itself at once into two parts; one of them is stored up in the vibrations of the slower kind, the other of the faster. If R is nearer to P than to Q the slower tends to preponderate and vice versâ.

The sound that is made when a bar is struck in this way is due to the regular disturbance of the form of the bar, which disturbance sets up pulses in the air, that is to say, sound waves. The disturbance itself consists in an alternating movement of the bar between two positions in which it is bent as shown in Fig. 85. The lower note is due to the blow at P, because the bar is in that case more easily bent. The disturbance may also be thought of as a pulse running up and down the bar. It is set in motion by the blow and travels with a speed depending on the stiffness of the bar on the one hand and its massiveness on the other. When it arrives at an end of the bar it is reflected. This way of representing the disturbance is equivalent to the other if due account is taken of the complicated process of reflection at the ends which is not so simple as in the case of a

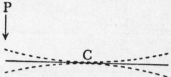

Fig. 85. The vibrating bar of Fig. 84 takes alternately the two forms shown by the dotted lines.

stretched string. If the bar were infinitely long, the pulses due to the stroke would run along it and never return, so that there would be no sound. One pulse, namely that which is caused by a stroke at P, moves slower than that which is caused by a stroke at Q. The latter therefore would leave the former behind.

Light traversing a crystal shows the analogous effect. If it travels along a line, forming a ray, its vibrations are in one or other or both of two directions which are at right angles to each other. There is something in the crystal corresponding to the stiffness in the bar, so that the two vibrations travel at different rates and one gets ahead of the other. It happens that in Iceland spar the 'stiffness' is least for vibrations which are perpendicular to the axis, and is the same for all such vibrations, just as the conductivity was the same for all such directions in the Senarmont experiment (Plate XVIIIc). Consequently, one of the vibrations in a ray travelling in any direction is perpendicular to the axis. In Fig. 77, for example, it is perpendicular to the plane of the paper. The other must be perpendicular to the first as in the case of the bar. If this one happens to be parallel to the axis it travels at the fastest speed of which it is capable within the crystal: and the nearer it comes to

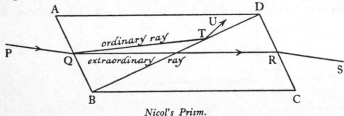

Nicol's Prism.

Fig. 86. A long piece of Iceland spar is cut into two pieces which are cemented by Canada balsam. The cut is so made in relation to the form of the crystal that only one of the two rays into which incident light is divided is able to get through the apparatus.

that parallelism the faster it travels   That is why the surface of its spread is a spheroid and its axial direction is the same as that of the crystal. The former vibration travels at the same rate whatever the direction of the ray and so its outward spread is described in terms of spheres. Thus the problem of Huygens is solved, in the sense that an explanation can be given in terms of mechanical effects and laws which are well-known.

Experimental work with polarised light is greatly facilitated by the use of a device due to William Nicol. A piece of Iceland spar is cut in two and cemented together again by Canada balsam: the cut is made along the line BD in Fig. 86. Now light travels in the balsam at a greater rate than one of the two rays in the spar, namely the one which is called the ordinary ray, and obeys the regular laws of refraction: but the rate in balsam is less than that of the other ray in the spar. Both rays travel at the same rate in the balsam; polarisation does not affect the rate at which light travels in a liquid. It is only in crystals that the speed of travel is affected by the relation between the direction of vibration and the crystal form. By the ingenious disposition which is represented in Fig. 86, the ordinary ray meets

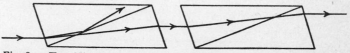

Fig. 87. Two Nicol prisms are similarly arranged. The first divides the incident light into two parts, and allows one of them to pass: the second makes no further subdivision, nor does it stop the ray that has passed through the first. But if the second is turned round through 90° about a line parallel to the long edges, the pair between them intercept all the light.

the Canada balsam at such an angle that it is totally reflected (see Fig. 45), while the other ray goes on. Half the energy of the original ray is thus absorbed in the Nicol's arrangement, while the rest emerges in the form of polarised light. Good pieces of spar are rare, and a large Nicol's prism is very valuable.

If as in the diagram (Fig. 87) a light ray is made to pass through two Nicol prisms in succession, the amount of light that emerges finally depends on the arrangement of the prisms. If the first is so set that the vibrations of the light that gets through it are – let us say – in the plane of the diagram, then if the second is disposed exactly as the first, the light will go through the second without any further loss. But if the second be turned round through a right angle, it will entirely absorb the polarised ray that falls upon it and no light emerges

from the pair. The effect is shown in the photographs
of Plate XIXA, B.

With the help of a Nicol we can even demonstrate,
more easily than before, the polarisation of light reflected
from a transparent surface.

The beam of polarised light falls upon a piece of glass at
G (Fig. 88). The Nicol is then gradually turned upon its

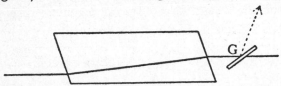

Fig. 88. The figure shows a polarised ray meeting a piece of plane glass,
and experiencing a feeble reflection: nearly all the light goes through. But
if the piece of glass – or the Nicol – is turned through 90° about the line of
the ray which is passing through it in the diagram, the reflection becomes
strong. The experiment of Malus.

axis and it appears that when the principal section of
the Nicol is in the plane of the paper, as shown by
the diagram, the reflection is poor; but when the
Nicol has been turned round through a right angle
from this position the reflection is strong. This implies, according to our conception of the way in
which polarisation takes place within a crystal, that
light is best reflected by a piece of glass when the
vibrations are parallel to its surface. (See also Plate
XVIIIB.) The glass plate should make an angle of
about 35° with the ray of light. We are repeating the
experiment of Malus.

Since light reflected from the surfaces of transparent
substances is polarised more or less, the many natural
reflections at the surface of the sea and other waters
must cause the effect to be not uncommon. We may

PLATE XIX

A

B

A ray of light emerging from one Nicol prism passes through a second when the two are set parallel to each other. The white arrow stuck on each prism lies in the principal plane of the crystal. The ray fails to get through the second when it is set perpendicular to the first. The paths of the rays are made visible by means of smoke in the air.

(*p.* 192)

remind ourselves, however, that the eye cannot detect polarisation directly: use must be made of a polarising device like the Nicol prism or the piece of glass held at the proper angle. It is possible when standing in certain positions near a picture to get rid of the troublesome glass reflections by looking through a Nicol prism and turning it round until it extinguishes the reflections, which it can do because they are polarised. But it is only possible to achieve this when the observer stands in the proper positions, and is not a practical help to the visitor to the gallery. It is possible in the same way to extinguish – in certain cases – the light reflected from the surface of the sea and to look down into its depths: and sometimes the method has been used by the observer in an aeroplane. But again the plan is not very practicable.

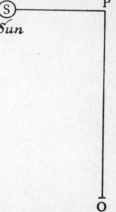

Fig. 89. The observer at o is looking up at the sky in the direction O P. If he places a Nicol prism before his eye, so that the principal plane – A B C D of Fig. 86 – is in the plane O P S, which contains O P and the line joining the observer to the sun at S, the sky appears dark. If the prism is turned about its axis through a right angle the sky brightens again.

The Polarisation of Light from the Sky

There is one extremely interesting case of the natural occurrence of polarisation, namely, in the light of the sky. It is interesting in the first place because it illustrates once more the capacity of the wave theory to explain natural facts, and in the second place, because its experimental investigation has been very ingenious, and moreover, has led to some very beautiful demonstrations.

The polarisation of the light from the sky is easily observed by the aid of a Nicol's prism (Fig. 89). Suppose that S is the sun, P a scattering particle, and O the eye of the observer. If the prism is so held that the principal section of the prism is in the same plane as SP and PO, then the sky appears dark. But if the prism is turned through a right angle about its axis, it appears bright. The same experiment may of course be made with a piece of glass but not, it is to be observed, with a silvered mirror. If the arrangement is as in Fig. 90, the eye at E will see a reflection in the mirror at M: but if the stand carrying the mirror is turned through a right angle so that the latter faces us as we look at the diagram the reflection grows darker.

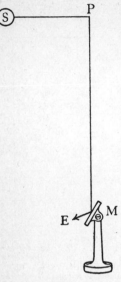

Fig. 90. Instead of a Nicol the observer may use a piece of unsilvered glass M as in Plate XVIIIB and reflect the light into his eye at E. With the arrangement in the figure he obtains a brighter reflection of the sky than if he turns the glass mirror about the line P M or about the vertical direction of its stand so that he himself when observing the reflection has to look in a direction perpendicular to the plane of the diagram.

We have been supposing that the vibrations of the light that get through the prism take place in the principal plane. Thus the vibrations of the waves that are scattered by P towards the mirror or the eye in these figures are perpendicular to the plane of the paper.

Now the wave theory leads us to expect that this would be the case. The point may be made clear by an analogy.

Two ropes, say twenty or thirty feet long, are tied at their middle points and held moderately taut by four men, one at each of the ends (Fig. 91). The man at A

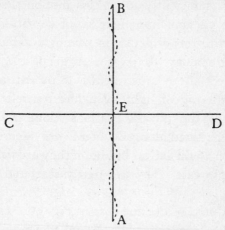

Fig. 91. Two ropes knotted together at E and held at the four ends. If a vibration in the plane of the diagram, as indicated by the wavy line, is originated at A, it will set B E in motion but not E C, nor E D: but if the vibration is perpendicular to the plane, E C and E D will be set into motion as well as E B.

sends a series of pulses along the rope in the direction AE. In the first instance, they are vertical vibrations, up and down. When they arrive at E, and the knot at that point begins vertical movements, pulses travel in consequence along EC and along ED; the original movement is also propagated along EB. But if the vibration which A gives to the rope is from side to side, as indicated by the dotted line, then no motion is transmitted along EC and ED because E cannot move in any way which will cause transverse movements to run along EC and ED, unless the original vibration sent by A has some up and down component in it. In this second case, a certain movement does go through E to the part EB and the pulses sent by A get through to B as a transverse movement continuing that along AE, because the knot at E yields sufficiently to let this motion through. In the actual phenomenon there is, of course, nothing to correspond to this difficulty in passing E which appears in the rope analogy. Light from A gets past E in all cases.

The object of the experiment is to present an analogy to the scattering of light by a fine particle such as a molecule of the air. Vibrations along AE are dispersed or scattered along EC or ED provided they are at right angles to the latter, but not if they are parallel. In intermediate cases they are partly scattered along EC and ED.

Now let us consider the case of Fig. 90. Light waves are sent out from the sun at S and move along SP. If their vibrations are in the plane of the paper, they do not start a transverse vibration which can move along PM: this corresponds to the first case of Fig. 91. But if the vibrations are perpendicular to the plane of the paper, they are able, when they meet the scattering particle at P, to start transverse waves along PM, again as in the case of the ropes. The original light from the sun which travels along SP must be supposed to contain transverse waves of every kind: that which runs along PM will consist specially of waves in which the vibrations are perpendicular to the plane of the diagram. The light of the sky is therefore polarised.

Some very beautiful laboratory demonstrations of these points can be given. Light from a lantern is polarised by the Nicol's prism N and reflected by a silvered mirror M arranged so as to send the reflected beam downwards into the jar J (Fig. 92). The reflected

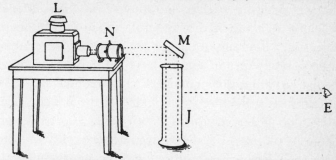

Fig. 92. Light from the lantern L is polarised by the Nicol prism N and reflected by the mirror M into the tall jar, which is filled with liquid containing finely divided matter in a state of suspension. The amount of light scattered varies with the direction of scattering as explained in the text.

ray is still polarised. Suppose, for example, that the vibrations are horizontal and perpendicular to the plane of the diagram when leaving the prism: they will still be so when traversing the jar. Let the jar be filled with clean water in which a little gum mastic has been dissolved: the gum is held in suspension in the form of very fine particles. These scatter the light: but not equally all round. To an eye at E in the plane of the paper the jar will seem to be luminous. But if the observer walks round the jar so that he now regards it from the side, as the diagram on this page is regarded, the jar appears dark. The same alteration takes place if the observer stands still and the Nicol's prism is turned round. If there are various observers in the room, the jar seems bright to some and dark to others.

The effect is very striking: and, in a varied form, it is extraordinarily beautiful. A quantity of sugar is dissolved in the jar. Sugar, like many other substances, has a curious effect on polarised light which is passing through it, in solid or in solution. The direction of vibration changes along the path, going round it as if on a screw. When the light enters the sugar solution at the bottom of the jar the vibrations are, let us say, at right angles to the plane of the paper in Fig. 92. As the light descends in the jar the vibrations change their direction and at a certain depth they are *in* the plane of the paper. The eye no longer receives scattered light. Lower down again the brightness of the jar seems to the eye at E to be restored. Now these alternations occur at intervals which vary with the wave-length, the blue being screwed round much faster than the red: and as a result the jar is filled with a gorgeous display of colour, increasing in intensity from the top to the bottom. Colour can be made to fill the whole jar from the top downwards by placing a quartz plate in the path of the light between the prism and the jar. Such a plate, cut at right angles to the axis of the crystal has the power, like sugar, to cause a rotation of the direction of vibration; and its introduction, therefore, causes the various wave-lengths to be already separated when they enter the jar.

CHAPTER VII

LIGHT FROM THE SUN AND THE STARS

STARS appear to us as bright points which move together across the sky. Astronomers have shown us long ago that in so doing they are telling us of the rotation of the earth rather than of their own movements. Very patient and skilled observation shows that there are relative motions amongst them, yet so small that the constellations have retained their form since man was first able to describe them. In the last hundred years the power of interpreting the messages brought by light has increased greatly. We are in touch with the stars. They are no longer a mere medley of bright points irregularly spread over the sky; nor even of suns that emit light like ours and are scattered through the depths of space. They have become to us parts of an active universe of which our own solar system is also a part. We can measure their distances, their weights, their luminosities, their compositions, their movements, and even estimate their historic past and their future. Our world of knowledge and perception has suddenly increased, and we begin to have understanding of its greater laws.

The very ancient science of astronomy has in times past relied almost entirely upon observations of the positions of the heavenly bodies. Light has been used as a means of measuring angles and so of plotting the apparent motions of sun, moon and stars upon a celestial sphere. The very great extension of astronomical knowledge which has occurred in the last hundred years had its beginnings in the examination of light itself and not only of the direction from which it came. The quality of the light from the sun, and its intensity are characteristic of the nature and physical conditions of the source: their study provides new means of enquiry, and at the same time, gives new possibilities to the means that have been so long in use.

The Distances of the Stars

The older observations could, and did, afford opportunities for measuring distances in space. Such measurements are of the highest importance and interest: it is a natural source of wonder that the stars are not merely bright spots on a sphere of which the earth is the centre, but bodies to be ranked with the sun in magnitude and temperature and other qualities, spread through vast spaces and not confined to a single sheet. Therefore, one of the first efforts of the astronomer has been to determine distances: and it is still one of his most exacting tasks.

To begin with, it is necessary to choose a unit of length. The measurement of distance necessarily takes the form of comparison with some standard unit: and this unit must be in a form which the astronomer can handle. Bars of metal prepared and maintained with extreme care by the government officials of various countries serve as the basis of all measurements of length, the standard metre and the standard yard being the two which are most in use, almost to the exclusion of all others. From these units the astronomer has a long way to go before he comes to the measurement of the great distances of the stars. The journey must be accomplished in stages, each of which results in the knowledge of some definite distance in terms of the unit, and each distance is at least some thousands of times as great as that which has been measured in the previous stage.

First, the surveyor is entrusted with the task of finding the number of times which the unit is contained within a length of some miles drawn upon the surface of the earth, in a north and south direction. At the two ends of this line the astronomer sets up his telescopes and measures the difference in latitude. He might, for example, choose a star which at a certain moment is due south of both observatories, to which therefore the measured line would point. At that moment the height of the star above the horizon would be observed in both telescopes; the height being measured in degrees. The difference in the two angles is known as the difference in latitude. If the earth were flat there would be no difference, because the direction of the horizon would then be the same for both places and the star is so far away. The amount of the difference in the actual case depends on the curvature of the earth, and can be used to measure the curvature.

Thus if P, Q (Fig. 93) are the two points on the earth's surface, and PS_1, and QS_2, the lines pointing to the star S, lines which are practically parallel, and if PH_1, QH_2 are the horizontal lines at P and Q, then the difference between the two measured angles S_1PH_1 and S_2QH_2 is the angle between PH_1 and QH_2; and this is the angle between the lines drawn from P and Q to the centre of the earth. Thus PQ and the angle PCQ are both known, and therefore PC, the radius of the earth is found. The earth is not quite round: it is a spheroid and not a sphere.

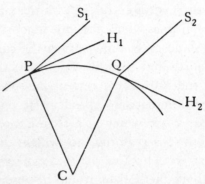

Fig. 93. An observer at P sees the horizon in the direction P H1. The angle s1 P H1 is the angular height of the star s above the horizon. The angle s2 Q H2 is the angular height of the same star as observed by an observer at Q. The difference between these angles is the angle P C Q, which is the difference in latitude of the two observers.

The polar radius is 3,950 miles almost exactly, and the equatorial radius is about 13 miles more.

This completes the next stage: the earth itself becomes a base line for wider measurements, because now that its form is known the actual distance between any two points upon it can be calculated from measurements of latitude and longitude, measurements which can be made with the aid of telescopes and clocks only: there is no need to measure such distances step by step with a metre or a yard rule.

In such measurements as these, we find the use of the telescope as an instrument of precision. It is not merely a magnifying instrument as most of us employ it. To the astronomer it is far more. The object glass makes a picture of some part of the heavens at its focus in the manner explained in Chapter II. A set of fine wires or spider threads can be arranged in the same focus so that the eye, with the aid of the eyepiece sees them both together: and the telescope may be moved until the star or other object under investigation falls on some one of the lines. If now the motion is renewed until some other star falls on the same line, the amount of that motion can be measured in terms of the angular scales attached to the telescope. In another class of experiments the telescope may be left fixed, and the apparent movement of the stars may be followed until another star lies upon the line; in this way the time of rotation of the earth enters in. Such measurements have been improving for centuries and have now reached a high degree of perfection: on which account the astronomer has been able to extend his measurements further and further into space.

The next stage is the measurement of the distances of the moon and the sun: the latter being the one that is necessary for still further advance. If the time at which the moon passes some definite mark in the sky, say a star or the edge of the sun during an eclipse, is observed at two different points on the earth's surface, it becomes possible to calculate the distance of the moon from the earth. For such measurements give the velocity of the moon, in much the same way as the speed of a car is found from the time observations of two policemen a known distance apart.

In the diagram PM_1 and QM_2 are parallel, or if only approximately so the fact may be allowed for, and so $M_1 M_2$ is equal to PQ, a known distance on the surface of the earth. The velocity of the moon then being known and also the time taken to go round the earth, the radius of the orbit can be calculated at once (Fig. 94).

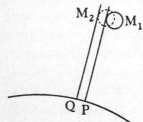

Fig. 94. To the observer at P the star s appears to be eclipsed by the moon when the latter is in the position M1; at Q the eclipse takes place when the moon is at M2. The distance M1 M2 is the same as P Q, which is known. Hence the velocity of the moon is found.

In much the same way, though the calculation is not so direct, the distance of the sun from the earth is derived from observations on the times when Venus or Eros appear to enter and leave the sun's disc, as they do occasionally, the observers being at known distances apart upon the earth. The difference to be observed is very small: even if the observers were at the opposite ends of the earth and could then make good measurements it would only amount to about five minutes.

In this way the radius of the earth's orbit has been found to be nearly 93 million miles. And now the astronomer has acquired a base line from which he can make his final leap into the spaces of the stars.

The value of such a base line in determining the relative motions of the earth and the stars was appreciated long before it could be made the base of any calculation.

To use a simple analogy due to Jeans,[1] a child in a swing sees the nearer objects around him move to and fro on a background of objects that are farther away. So observers on the earth should see some of the stars move to and fro with respect to others, the movement keeping time with the swing of the earth in its orbit about the sun. No one made a successful observation of this kind until 1838, for the simple reason that the motion to be observed was excessively minute, far smaller than was expected and much beyond the powers of detection of comparatively inefficient instruments. In that year three stars, 61 Cygni, ∝ Centauri and ∝ Lyræ were found to be executing motions against the celestial background, which, though exceedingly small, were unmistakable. These stars are so far away that their light takes several years to reach us: in the case of ∝ Centauri, for example, the time is 4.31 years. The immensity of the distance is best realised if this time is compared with the 500 seconds which light takes to travel 93 million miles on its way to the earth.

Only a few of the nearest stars can be treated in this way. The rest are so distant that the finest telescopes can see no difference in their positions when viewed from opposite points of the earth's orbit. It is marvellous that so much has been done in respect even to these few, for, roughly speaking, they are a million times as far from us as the nearest planets. The astronomer speaks of their distances in terms of light years.

[1] *The Universe Around Us.*

The Velocity of Light

We have not hitherto considered the value of the velocity of light: none of the visible effects we have been discussing are concerned with its actual magnitude. But we must now form some idea of the velocity if the term 'light year' is to have any definite meaning.

The time taken by light to travel a measured distance upon the earth is so very small that it can be detected only by instruments of great precision: Galileo tried such an experiment and failed. It is not surprising that the first measurements, which supplied indeed the first proofs that light had a velocity, were made in connection with the time taken by light to travel over the 186 million miles of the diameter of the earth's orbit.

According to the often told story, Olaf Römer at the end of the 17th century was observing in Paris the times of eclipse of Jupiter's moons behind his disc. From a series of observations he calculated the average time of rotation of each moon. He then observed that when the earth and Jupiter were at their least distance from each other, each eclipse occurred about eight minutes before the time calculated on a basis of averages. When the two planets were as far from each other as possible each eclipse was eight minutes too late. He rightly concluded that the variations from the calculated result were due to the fact that light took time to cross the orbit of the earth. It is easy to imagine a simple analogy. If a business man in England were in the habit of receiving a letter from Australia every week, which letter was always forwarded on to him wherever he might be, and

if he were in the habit of travelling backwards and forwards between London and Dublin, he would get his
letter before the average time if it came to him in London
and after that time if he were in Dublin: and the difference between the time taken by a letter to reach him
in Dublin and the corresponding time for London would
be the time taken by the letter to go from London to
Dublin. In this way, since it takes 1,000 seconds nearly
to cross the earth's orbit, if this be assumed to be 186
million miles the velocity of light will be 186,000 miles
a second. There are other ways of determining this
magnitude, and it is now known very accurately. This
is the velocity of all waves in the ether of space: in transparent bodies like glass and water it is somewhat less,
and the air a very little less. It is often pointed out that
this being so the music transmitted by radio may reach
distant countries by way of waves in the ether before,
being carried by sound waves in the air, they reach the
other end of the concert hall.

In these applications of the measuring rod to the
spacings of the stars, light is used as a means of determining direction only. It has served this purpose for
thousands of years, though not very effectively until
Galileo first used the telescope. And still the continuous
improvement of the telescope increases the accuracy of
the angular measurements and adds to the value of the
observations. On the other hand, it is quite a new
science which observes the quality of the light from a star
and draws inferences therefrom as to its nature and
movements.

The Analysis of the Light from the Stars

The first step in the acquirement of this knowledge is made when we use a prism or a grating to analyse the light. In every case we find the same spectrum colours, running from red to violet, for our eyes perceive these alone of the complex which each star emits. But the emphasis in different parts of the spectrum is not always the same: it varies from star to star. A blue star is always hotter than a red star. The temperature of the star can in fact be determined from the position of greatest emphasis. This would not be possible were it not for a very remarkable natural law, namely, that the quality of the light emitted by a substance depends only, except in special cases, on the temperature and not upon the nature of the substance. If, for example, we gaze into a hollow in a glowing coal fire, a red hot cave with as small an opening as possible, where everything is at the same high temperature, we do not see the outlines of the pieces of coal inside, nor of pieces of metal or china if they are well inside the hole and have acquired the fire temperature. Being at the same temperature, coal, metal and china all send out radiation of the same quality and so they cannot be distinguished from one another. In a furnace where the temperature is raised by a blast the quality of the light is not the same as that of the light from a coal fire. It is whiter because the emphasis has been shifted towards the blue end of the spectrum: more blue rays are present. If a temperature of 6000° Centigrade could be reached the light would have the quality of daylight because that is the temperature approximately of the sun. Some of the stars are hotter still and the blue rays increase still more in relative intensity. Thus the temperature of a star is told by the quality of its spectrum, that is to say, by the relative distribution of energy among the various wavelengths. This implies previous determinations in the laboratory of the way in which the quality varies with temperature, and since laboratory temperatures cannot match those of the hot stars there is some uncertainty in the star measurements. It is necessary to assume that a law which holds over the laboratory range will hold also for temperatures beyond the range of actual experiment. Examples of star spectra are given in Plate XXA.

A very simple experiment illustrates this connection between quality and temperature. We throw upon the screen the spectrum of the light from an electric arc, and then cut off the current. As the glow of the carbon fades and its temperature declines, we see that the spectrum disappears but the blue goes first and the red last.

Spectrum Analysis Applied to the Stars

By a still closer observation of the spectrum of a star we can find its nature. When the light is analysed by the prism, it is found that the spectrum is, allowing for the effects of temperature, like that of any other glowing mass, as for example, the carbon in the arc lamp, with an important exception. A number of clearly defined ranges of wave-length, generally exceedingly narrow ranges, are missing.

We have met already with such cases of absorption of

radiation when considering the origin of colour: there is here however a difference in that the abstractions from the spectrum are so very precise and sharply defined and are generally so numerous. Illustrations of this peculiarity may be seen in the reproductions of spectra in Plate XXA.

The explanation is ready to hand: we can base it on the analogies which we used before, namely, those of the tuning forks, and the wireless sets. We must look rather more closely into the comparison than previously, because we need to see the important connection between sender and receiver in the various modes of radiation, sound, radio waves, and light.

Our first point is simple enough. A single tuning fork gives out a very pure note: in other words, the sound which it emits consists of air waves of a definite frequency. This sound wave spreads out in all directions. If in one direction it passes by another tuning fork of exactly the same pitch, it will set this second fork going and of course it will spend energy in doing so. Thus the sound travelling in this special direction is weakened : there has been absorption. Nor is this loss made up by the sounding of the second fork, because the latter spreads its sound in all directions and cannot make good the loss in the particular direction. This is the basis of the absorption and production of colour, as we have seen already. It will be observed that the emitter and receiver are of the same pitch. Just so a radio station emits waves which are sharply adjusted within a certain range of frequency: if care were not taken in this respect broadcasting would be impossible. And if the receiver can be sharply tuned to the same frequency, it will absorb some of the energy distributed from the central station, which energy is diminished thereby. A wireless set can be made to radiate at least feebly, and if it does it emits waves of exactly the same pitch as that of the sending station to which it responds. Some wireless sets as we know can be tuned very sharply: if the radio station is sending out waves which adhere closely to their proper frequency such sets will only respond if the tuning is carefully done, and then the response will be strong.

In the same way an atom may be set into vibration by heating the body or gas of which it is a part. If the radiation which it emits meets a number of atoms capable of vibrating with exactly the same frequency – or it may be frequencies – its energy is absorbed in part and passes on diminished. And here again the matter of the exactness of tuning is important. An atom by itself, uninfluenced by neighbours, is like a good radio transmitter, its emitted vibrations lie within a very narrow range. We should say ranges rather than range, because an atom should be compared rather with a bell or a violin string than a tuning fork. The fork is exceedingly simple, emitting little more than one note; whereas bell and string and atom each emit a number of notes at one and the same time. Each note, however, is very sharply defined and can be tuned to with great exactness. This sharpness of tuning is characteristic of the atoms in a gas, for in this condition the atoms are independent of one another for most of the time: collisions occur, but the times during which the atoms are so close to one another as to influence each other's vibrations do not last long.

Thus a multitude of atoms forming a gas will resemble a good radio station if they are emitting, and a good or 'selective' wireless set if they are receiving.

If then a ray of light containing all frequencies passes through a crowd of such 'selective' atoms there will be a sharp absorption or selection of particular frequencies, and the spectrum will show a number of narrow gaps, as illustrated in Plate XXA. If the gas is emitting, it will send out light of the same frequencies as that which it absorbs. This effect is shown in Plate XXB.

The Spectrum of the Sun

The spectrum of the sun shows an immense number of these sharply defined gaps or 'lines' as they are generally called. When the temperatures of various substances, iron, calcium, hydrogen, etc., are raised by heating until they become luminous vapours, it is found that they emit, each of them, light of a certain number of sharply defined frequencies. It is also found that these correspond line by line to the lines in the spectrum of the sun. The conclusion is obvious: the light from the sun must have gone through clouds of these atoms somewhere, and in respect to such substances as iron or calcium, or most other elements, this must have happened on the sun because in no other part of the path of the light has there been enough heat to bring the substances to the state of a luminous gas. If therefore, the spectra of the sun and stars and other luminous bodies be analysed and compared with the spectra emitted in the laboratory by the various elements brought to the condition of luminous gases, it becomes possible at once to say whether or no these elements exist in the heavenly bodies as well as on the earth. These investigations were first carried out on the great scale by the enthusiasm of Huggins, Lockyer and their contemporaries. From that time to this they have increased in interest and importance because it has been found that there is far more in them than mere correspondences between the positions of definite frequencies in the two classes of spectra. The frequencies characteristic of each element depend on the condition of the element, which may be stripped of one or more of its electrons and at each such alteration may alter its notes: the condition depends on the temperature and the density of the gas, and thus the analysis of stellar spectra gives information of the state of the star as well as of its composition.

The elements that are found on the earth are found also in the stars. In one notable case the existence of an element was proved by Lockyer's observation of the sun's spectrum before it had been handled in the laboratory. Certain well marked lines were found which corresponded to nothing then known, and Lockyer deduced the presence of some new substance which he called 'helium': it was not until long afterwards that it was extracted from cleveite and other minerals. It is now well known as the best gas for the inflation of dirigible balloons, since it is almost as much lighter than air as hydrogen is, and it is not inflammable. In the laboratory it is an object of extraordinary interest, since the atom of helium is the alpha particle which radioactive substances emit. On account of the tremendous speed of its emission it can enter the domains of other atoms and make its way into the very nucleus, which it may even break, and by which it is usually deflected. Observations of these effects were the main origin of the modern atomic theories, for in the hands of Rutherford and his fellow workers they established the nuclear theory of atomic structure and all that has been built thereon.

But now there is one very important question to which some answer must be found. We have supposed that a radiation is emitted by the sun, which would have given a complete spectrum, were it not that on its way to us it has passed through an atmosphere surrounding the sun and containing the various elements in the form of gases. These gases themselves must be luminous and be emitting light of the very frequencies which we suppose them to have been absorbing and therefore causing black lines to appear in the spectrum. What is the origin of the original radiation? It must be so plentiful that its absorption in the sun's atmosphere makes a difference which the luminosity of the atmosphere itself does not make good. And its energy is distributed all over the spectrum: it is not limited to a number of definite frequencies.

We have already seen that independent atoms would issue their proper frequencies exactly. But they are not wholly independent: they spend a certain fraction of their time in each other's neighbourhood when their motions cause them to collide. During those moments they do not issue their proper frequencies so strictly. If they are so crowded together as to spend a large part of their time under each other's influence the ranges of proper

frequency will spread until they meet and overlap and
the whole spectrum is emitted. In a roughly analogous
way, if a number of tuning forks, each on its stand, were
thrown anyhow into a box which was then shaken violently, a medley of jangling sound would issue which
would no longer be confined to the particular notes of the
tuning forks. In the body of the sun the atoms are

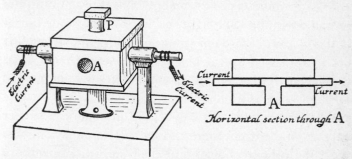

Fig. 95. The little furnace is made of refractory materials. Inside it an
arc is formed by the electric current. Metals are dropped in at the hole on
top. When the hole is left open the vapours escape and the light that issues
at A can be resolved into a bright line spectrum. When the plug P is inserted,
the vapour fills the tunnel ending in A, and the light has to go through it.
Dark lines now appear in the spectrum where there were bright lines before.

crowded together and violently agitated by the tremendous temperature: and it is in this way that we can account
for the continuity of the spectrum. The somewhat
cooler atmosphere surrounding the sun removes certain
frequencies and hence the spectrum lines.

We can imitate these conditions by a laboratory
experiment. A small electric furnace is made by passing
the current through two carbon pencils which are
inserted in the walls of the fire-clay enclosure, as shown
in Fig. 95. The pencils are first made to touch and
then drawn somewhat apart in the usual way. A piece

of sodium is placed in the arc. Then intensely yellow vapour rises up in a cloud and leaves the furnace at the top: a small tunnel-like opening at the side of the furnace allows the light from the arc to pass through a lens and a prism and so to form a spectrum upon the screen. The bright yellow line of sodium is very conspicuous. We now stop up the opening over the arc and the incandescent gas can only find its way out at the second opening. The light has then to cross some inches of this vapour before emerging: and now the yellow line has disappeared and a black line appears in its place: the vapour has taken out of the light from the arc the very frequencies which it emits itself.

When there is a total eclipse of the sun the incandescent vapours of its atmosphere can be seen to extend far beyond the obscured disc: and their spectra consist of a series of bright lines as we should expect.

It is an interesting and important point that a luminous gas which gives a 'bright line' spectrum will give a full spectrum if there is enough of the gas. There is always a certain amount of general radiation as well as that of particular frequencies of the atoms of which the gas is made. Now the latter is absorbed in going through the gas more than the former, and so it happens that it comes only from the external layers, while the latter, the general radiation, can come from greater depths. If the depth of the gas is great enough the two effects compensate so as to give equal weight to the two varieties of radiation, and the spectrum is complete. It becomes that which is characteristic of the temperature and is independent of the nature of the emitting body.

Thus the completeness of the spectrum of a heavenly body does not mean that it is a solid, but merely that there is enough of it.

The Motions of the Stars to and from the Earth

By another form of careful observation it is possible to determine the rate at which a star is approaching or receding from the earth. For if, say, the star is rushing towards the earth it is crushing up the waves from the rear and all the wave-lengths are artificially shortened, and become more refrangible. Just so an approaching motor-car crushes up the sound waves, and, as it recedes, draws them out. All day the motor-cars go by and the pitches of all the noises made by a car drop at the moment of passing. If the car is travelling at 25 miles an hour the drop is nearly a semi-tone. If the star gave a complete spectrum free from lines we should not be able to detect this shift, because the wave-lengths that gave the extreme violet would have been shortened and become invisible, while at the red end wave-lengths just too long to be visible would now be shortened and enter the red. All the wave-lengths would be shortened some-what, both visible and invisible: but the visible colours would be supplied to our eyes just the same, and we should see no change. There is however an observable shift in the lines of the spectrum, an effect which was first described by Doppler. And as the positions of the lines can be very exactly measured, and as the shift is proportional to the speed of the star relative to the earth, it becomes possible to measure the relative motion of the two bodies along the line joining them.

An illustration of this effect is given in Plate XXc. The two spectra that are shown in this illustration are due to light received from the two edges of the sun, eastern and western. In one case, the source of light is coming towards the earth, on account of the sun's revolution, in the other it is receding. In both cases the light has passed through the earth's atmosphere, and certain lines in the spectra are due to absorption by oxygen. The two spectra are put together so that these lines fit, so that the wave-lengths in the two correspond exactly. It will then be observed that other lines are slightly out of adjustment. These lines are due to absorption by the sun's atmosphere. The lack of adjustment is due to the Doppler effect, the lines being shifted slightly towards the short wave end in the case of light coming from the approaching edge of the sun and vice versâ. The presence of the oxygen lines makes it possible to register the two spectra exactly. The shifts in a star's spectrum are not so easily displayed as in this case. It is to be observed that the shift is the same for all the sun's lines.

These measurements are independent of distance and so arises the curious situation that, while most of the stars are too far away to be seen moving across the sky, motions of approach or recession can be measured with considerable accuracy. In this way for example, it is found that the distant nebulae, or at least the few that give enough light for the experiment, are receding: and apparently those that are furthest away are going the fastest, whence the modern conception of an expanding universe Many stars approach and recede at regular intervals: and it is clear that each such star has a dark companion about which it is revolving. But all such deductions belong to the fuller study of astronomy, and so do other questions such as the luminosity of the various stars and the inferences that can be drawn from a joint knowledge of luminosity and temperature. It is enough for our present purpose to have seen how full of information are the characteristics of the light that comes to us from all parts of the universe.

We may pause a moment here to consider a familiar peculiarity in the light from the stars. Their twinkling is an effect due to the want of uniformity of the atmosphere. It is analogous to the quivering of objects seen through the heated air above a fire in the open or a candle in the room. The rays of the star take a course which wavers somewhat on its way to the observer. Sometimes its light is partially cut off for a moment because some portion of the intervening atmosphere, differing slightly in refractivity from its surroundings, swings the rays to one side. Colour also appears, because the red rays that reach the eye from a star do not come by quite the same road as the blue, and the interfering portion of the atmosphere cuts out the one colour and not the other. This effect is not obvious to the eye gazing at the star, but is readily seen if the reflection of the star is observed in a mirror which is slightly and continuously shaken. The point of light is drawn out into a string of coloured jewels. A still closer examination by the aid of the spectroscope shows that the spectrum of the star is continuously traversed by dark patches which move from red to blue or from blue to red according as the star is in the west or the east. This is readily explained. As the earth revolves carrying its atmosphere with it, the interfering patch also moves from west to east. In the case of a star in the west therefore the patch interrupts the red first and the blue afterwards because the red rays from a star in the west come to the eye by a path which is more direct, and more to the west, than the path of the blue rays.

Invisible Radiation

We may now remove the limits we set ourselves at first and consider those wave-lengths which we cannot see with our eyes. And first we may think of those which lie close up to the visible range and on either side of it. Our dependence upon instruments is then complete. But fortunately, there are several ways in which this invisible radiation can be detected. Chief among these are the methods of photography. Plates can be sensitised so as to be responsive to many such qualities of radiation. In fact the ordinary forms of plate that have been in use for many years are particularly sensitive not only to the shorter waves of the spectrum but also to those which lie just outside and are known as the ultra-violet. The difficulty has been to render plates sensitive to the longer waves: but in recent years this has been successfully accomplished. Quite lately the results of this advance have attracted great interest. One of them illustrates excellently some of the points we were considering at an earlier stage.

We saw that the red rays were less turned aside by

PLATE XX

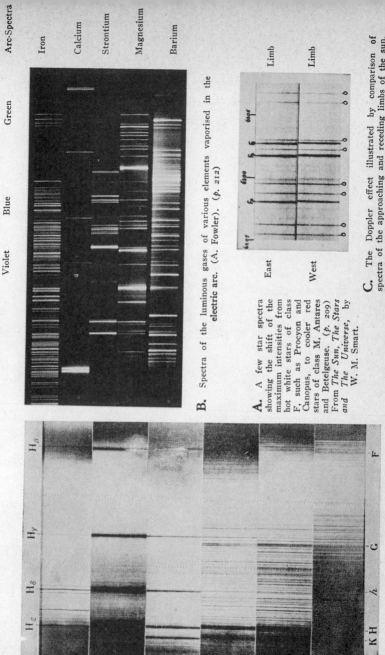

Arc-Spectra

Iron

Calcium

Strontium

Magnesium

Barium

B. Spectra of the luminous gases of various elements vaporised in the electric arc. (A. Fowler). (*p.* 212)

A. A few star spectra showing the shift of the maximum intensities from hot white stars of class F, such as Procyon and Canopus, to cooler red stars of class M, Antares and Betelgeuse. (*p.* 209) From *The Sun, The Stars and The Universe,* by W. M. Smart.

Limb

Limb

East

West

C. The Doppler effect illustrated by comparison of spectra of the approaching and receding limbs of the sun. The lines in each of the two photographs due to the oxygen of the earth's atmosphere being fitted together, the lines due to the iron in the sun do not fit. (*p.* 217)

Spectral Class

B

A

F

G

K

M

H_β H_γ H_δ H_ε

K H h G F

PLATE XXI

These photographs are due to the Ilford Company. The lower is taken with an infra-red filter, the other according to the usual conditions. Note that the blue sky appears black since it does not scatter infra-red rays. On the other hand, the grass and the trees reflect much infra-red and therefore appear white. The whole tone system is abnormal because the rays are not those which are used by the eye. Note also the extraordinary rendering of detail, especially in the far distance. (*p. 221*)

the atoms and molecules of the air and by the dust and vapour in the air than the blue rays at the other end of the spectrum. Consequently if a plate is sensitive to the red rays, and still more if its sensitivity extends into the infra-red, it can register the image formed in the camera of objects which to the eye are obscured by haze. Mountains have been photographed many scores of miles away. The recent issues of *The Times* have contained beautiful photographs of distant landscapes, e.g., across the English Channel, or the Irish Sea taken at a time when the eye could see nothing of them. The photographs of Plate XXI, due to the Ilford Company, are fine examples of this use of the infra-red rays. Of course the photographic camera always has one great advantage over the eye in that the strength of its impressions increases with time: an advantage of great value in astronomy also. Thus screens which may be used to cut out the shorter waves are not therefore useless if they cut down the red and infra-red rays to some extent: it is only necessary to increase the time of exposure. The waves are of course still small enough to render fine detail.

In these photographs green vegetation always comes out strongly. It will be remembered that chlorophyll does not absorb the deep red, and therefore the light reflected by leaves and grass has a strong effect on the specially prepared plates. In consequence of this action the trees, bushes and grass look as if they were covered with snow.

To the physicist the infra-red rays are of especial interest because they are due to the vibrations of molecules rather than of atoms, and their study helps to an understanding of molecular structure.

By the term 'ultra-violet rays' is meant generally the invisible part of the sun's radiation which reaches the earth's surface and consists of waves shorter than those that are visible. There must be wave-lengths still shorter in the light that leaves the sun, but the atmosphere absorbs them. The limit is 0.00003 cm, rather more than the hundred thousandth of an inch: no radiation of shorter wave-length reaches us on the surface of the earth. The absorption of the radiation heats the atmosphere, so that at heights of 100 miles and more above the earth's surface the air is much hotter than it is at the surface itself. Such a layer differs so much in condition from the air below that it reflects strongly both the radio waves and sound waves, as we have observed already.

Fluorescence

The ultra-violet rays have many energetic actions of which some are only beginning to be appreciated. One of the most remarkable is that of causing certain bodies to fluoresce, and this has been long known and used. If we throw the spectrum of an arc light upon a screen which has been painted with sulphate of quinine we see colour long past the violet end, in fact the ultra-violet becomes visible. This effect is greatly enhanced if we use lenses and prisms made of quartz instead of glass. Quartz allows the ultra-violet rays to pass far more freely than glass, which is indeed opaque to the shortest wave-lengths. It is to be remembered that glass is to us a transparent substance because it does not absorb the visible rays: but if our eyes were so constituted that we saw rather the ultra-violet, or, it might be, the infra-red, we should transfer the term, 'transparent' from glass to quartz in the one case, and to rock salt in the other.

When we look at the colour which appears all over the prepared screen where the ultra-violet light strikes it we see that it is of a bluish tinge throughout almost its whole extent. This blue is not a new colour at all: when examined by the spectroscope it is found to have a wave-length belonging to part of the visible spectrum. The ultra-violet has not become visible, but has excited a visible colour. Radiation of one wave-length has disappeared, and light of another has taken its place. This appears at first sight to contradict our experiences with wave motions: we have always assumed that neither reflection nor refraction nor diffraction changes the length of a wave, and have not observed any such effect in the course of our ordinary experiences. But there is no contradiction: our assumptions have been correct and conformable with experience. It is no ordinary reflection or refraction, but is, on the other hand, something very extraordinary indeed. In fact it is the first sign that our wave theory is incomplete: not that it is wrong, nor do we have to retract any of our statements about it. We find only that there are phenomena which we cannot make it cover: and as we proceed this will become more clear.

There is a very interesting laboratory experiment which illustrates the position we have reached in our present argument. Sunlight is introduced through a slit in the shutter of a darkened room: and by lenses and prisms a spectrum is thrown upon the surface of a basin of water, into which some eosin or other strongly fluorescent dye has been thrown (Plate Ic). The red and yellow rays go right through the liquid and strike the bottom of the basin: but all the rest are held up at the surface. Their colour has gone and in place of the green and blue there is a dark green strip which looks like a ribbon floating on the water. It extends far beyond the blue end of the spectrum as can easily be verified by floating a scrap of white paper into the coloured strip. If the slit is fine, the principal lines of the sun's spectrum are clearly seen: and some will appear in the ultra-violet portion, which further illustrates the point that there is no objective difference between the radiation that we can see and that which we cannot. The blue and green rays of the spectrum penetrate but a little way into the liquid: their conversion into rays of lower frequency is complete within a very short distance of the surface. The red rays go through with very little hindrance. It will be observed that there is a marked 'degradation' in this phenomenon: the disappearing colours are replaced by others which are on the whole nearer the red end of the spectrum. See also Plate XIVc.

Fluorescence is no uncommon effect: one of the readiest ways of observing it is to look at the surface of a mineral lubricating oil in a glass vessel, where the blue tinge is due to this fluorescent action.

As we have already observed, the air is a strong absorber of the very short wave-lengths, so that sunlight contains only such as do not fall below a certain limit.

Now we have many ways of producing waves shorter than any that reach us from the sun: and we find that the fluorescent action increases rapidly as the length is diminished. A mercury vapour lamp is a very strong source of short wave-lengths: which, if the tube in which the light is produced is made of quartz, emerge into the open. It is dangerous to the eyes to look at such a tube: the sunlight would also be injurious if the short wave-lengths were not absorbed by the atmosphere. Under the mercury vapour lamp many substances glow brilliantly, which show no such effect in daylight. The colours excited in this way are very various, and the whole effect is singularly beautiful. Screens can be made which intercept all the visible rays and allow only the ultra-violet to pass: in which case the fluorescing objects seem to be self-luminous. We may look towards the source of the rays, which of course we cannot see, for if we are at a little distance away the diminished rays will do no harm for a time. We then observe a strange effect: the whole room seems to be full of a luminous haze. It is due to fluorescence excited by the ultra-violet light in the humour of the eye: the effect is entirely subjective. If we interpose a screen so as to cut off the rays from our eyes the whole effect disappears.

The Discharge of Electricity by Ultra-Violet Light

Another remarkable property of ultra-violet light is its power of discharging negative electricity from certain metals on which it falls, particularly from the alkali metals and from zinc. This is readily demonstrated. An electrical machine is made to produce a succession of sparks between two knobs. One of the latter is of zinc, clean and freshly amalgamated with mercury: the machine is so worked that this is the negative knob. The other knob is connected to earth. Under these circumstances the machine loads up the prepared knob with negative electricity until the charge upon it puts the air between the knobs into a state of greater tension than it can bear: there is a breakdown and a spark passes.

If now the ultra-violet light from some source is thrown upon the zinc knob the sparking ceases. In fact the negative electricity cannot accumulate on the knob because the ultra-violet light discharges it as fast as it gathers. If a glass plate is put between the light and the knob the sparks start again, because the glass intercepts the rays though transparent to visible light. It is strange to see the sudden cessation and renewal of sparking as the glass is interposed and withdrawn.

From these and similar experiments we gather the impression that the shorter the wave-length the stronger is the action, and this suggests that the experiments should be repeated with wave-lengths that are as short as possible. By so doing we may be in a position to make some of the phenomena more obvious, and we may more easily come to a general understanding of them. This turns out to be the case. We employ the X-rays. We must first of all make sure that they can be considered as ether waves with as much justice as light. We can then consider their properties and we shall find there, exhibited much more vividly, the same phenomena as are shown by ultra-violet light. We shall see, to some extent at least, how the wave theory cannot take account

226

of many most striking facts of observation, and needs supplementing in some way which we do not perfectly understand as yet. We plunge into questions which, because they are not yet resolved, give our present researches an extraordinary fascination.

CHAPTER VIII

THE RÖNTGEN RAYS

IT was in 1895 that Röntgen discovered a new
form of radiation, to which, as its nature was so
uncertain, he gave the name of the X-ray. Its relation
to known forms of radiation became at once a subject
of the keenest investigation. Within a few weeks of his
discovery Röntgen established its principal characteristics, without coming to a definite conclusion as to its
nature. It was not until 1912, when von Laue showed it
could be diffracted like ordinary light, that it was recognised with certainty as an ether wave of extremely short
wave-length. Laue used a crystal for his diffraction
grating in a manner which we will presently examine.
The X-ray is therefore identical with light in respect to
its nature, but differs greatly in quality: a state of things
which is very favourable to an extension of our general
knowledge of such radiations. It is of particular interest
because a study of the shortened wave shows that our
wave theory, while confirmed in the applications we
have been making of it, is incomplete: it is incapable in
its old form of absorbing a very considerable number of
new facts. A more comprehensive scheme is shaping
itself slowly, and thus arises a situation of the greatest
interest.

The X-rays are generally produced as a consequence
of the electric spark or discharge in a space where the

pressure of the air or other gas is extremely low. The electric spark has for centuries been a subject of interested observation, but no great step forward was made until it was arranged that the discharge should take place in a glass tube or bulb from which the air had been pumped out more or less completely. The spark became longer, wider, and more highly coloured as the pressure

Fig. 96. The cathode or negative terminal is on the right at *a*. The rays proceed in straight lines across the tube and excite fluorescence on the opposite wall. A metal cross *b* casts a sharp shadow.

diminished. When Crookes so improved the air pump that pressures of the order of the millionth part of atmospheric pressure became attainable a phenomenon appeared which had not been previously observed. The negative terminal became the source of a radiation which shot in a straight line across the bulb and had mechanical effects. It generated heat whenever it struck the opposite wall or some body placed to intercept it: it excited vivid fluorescence in glass and many minerals: it could turn a light mill wheel if it struck the vanes. And, a most important property, the stream could be deflected by bringing a magnet near it. This was an extremely important observation for it suggested that the stream consisted of electrified particles in flight. Such a stream would be equivalent to an electric current and would therefore be susceptible to the force of a magnet. Illustrations of Crookes's experiments are given in Figures 96, 97, 98, and 99. They are taken from

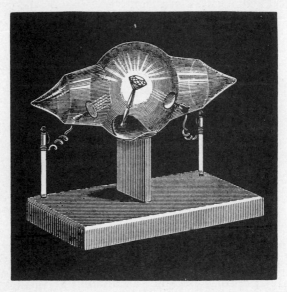

Fig. 97. The rays excite a vivid fluorescence in the diamond mounted in the centre of the tube.

the original blocks used in the published account of a discourse which he gave at the Royal Institution in April 1879. Crookes believed that the stream consisted of molecules of some kind. He argued that his air pump had attained such perfection that the comparatively few molecules left in the tube could move over distances comparable with the length of the tube without coming into collision with other molecules. Such a condition, he said, was as different from that of a gas as the latter from that of a liquid. At the end of a paper contributed to the Royal Society in the same year (1879) he wrote in a dim but interesting foreshadowing of the future which was partly to be verified:

'The phenomena in these exhausted tubes reveal to physical science a new world – a world where matter

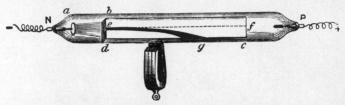

Fig. 98. The cathode rays are limited to a narrow pencil by means of a slot placed in front of the cathode at *a*. The deflections of the stream by a horse-shoe magnet are then observed easily.

exists in a fourth state, where the corpuscular theory of light holds good, and where light does not always move in a straight line; but where we can never enter, and in which we must be content to observe and experiment from the outside.'

J. J. Thomson, Wiechert and others showed that the stream consisted of particles carrying negative charges of electricity, and that these carriers were far smaller than even the hydrogen atom. The name 'electron' was given to them. It appeared that electrons could be torn away from any kind of atom, if sufficient electric force was supplied by the induction coil or other electric contrivance for producing the requisite power; and that the electrons from all sources were exactly alike. Evidently the electron was a fundamental constituent of matter. The stream of electrons was called the cathode ray because it issued from the negative or cathode terminal.

Röntgen was investigating the cathode ray phenomena when he found that photographic plates near by became fogged although no light could have reached them.

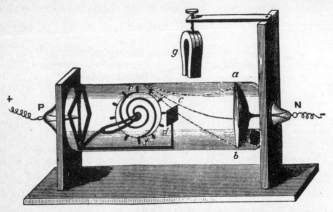

Fig. 99. The cathode *a* is made in the shape of a saucer: this is found to have the effect of concentrating the rays to a point. Normally a screen *c* intercepts the rays, but the magnet *g* deflects them so that they get over the top of the screen and strike the vanes of the little wheel *e f*, which then spins rapidly. If the disposition of the magnet is reversed, the rays go under *c* and the wheel spins the opposite way.

He traced the cause to a radiation issuing from his glass bulb, and in particular from the place where the cathode rays struck the wall: and proceeded to examine the general characteristics of the new rays upon which he had stumbled

In many respects they resembled light. They moved in straight lines and cast sharp shadows, they traversed space without any obvious transference of matter, they acted on a photographic plate, they excited certain materials to fluorescence, and they could, like ultra-violet

THE RÖNTGEN RAYS

light, discharge electricity from conductors. In other
ways the rays seemed to differ from light. The mirrors,
prisms and lenses which deflected light had no such
action on X-rays: gratings as ordinarily constructed
did not diffract them: neither double refraction, nor
polarisation was produced by the action of crystals.
Moreover they had an extraordinary power of penetrating matter. Nothing seemed to hold them up
entirely, though everything exerted some power of
absorption: heavier atoms were more effective than
lighter. Hence arose the quickly observed power of
revealing the inner constitution of bodies opaque to
light: bones cast shadows much deeper than those
due to the surrounding flesh.

If the velocity of X-rays could have been shown
without question to have been the same as that of light
it would have established their identity: but the experiment though attempted was too difficult. Barkla
showed that a pencil of X-rays could have 'sides' or be
polarised if the circumstances of their origin were properly arranged, but the polarisation differed in some of
its aspects from that which light could be made to ex-
hibit. Laue's experiment brought the controversy to
an end, by proving that a diffraction of X-rays could be
produced which was in every way parallel to the diffraction of light: if the diffraction phenomena could be depended upon to prove the wave theory of light, exactly
the same evidence existed in favour of a wave theory of
X-rays.

Laue's Experiment

Let us now consider the details of Laue's famous experiment which has had such striking consequences. The plan of it was very simple. A fine pencil of X-rays was to be sent through a crystal and a photographic

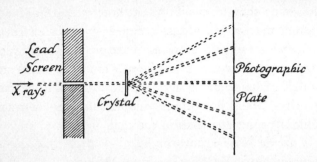

Fig. 100. The X-rays pass through a fine opening in a lead screen and impinge upon the crystal as shown. Laue's diffraction pattern is formed upon the photographic plate.

plate was to be placed to receive the pencil after it had emerged on the other side, Fig. 100. Laue surmised that beside the main image on the plate which would be caused by the incidence of the pencil there might be other subsidiary images. He based his forecast on a consideration of effects of this kind, which, as we have seen, occur in the case of light. When a train of ether waves falls upon a plate on which parallel lines are ruled, or is transmitted through such a plate, or passes through an atmosphere in which fine particles of uniform size are suspended, there are regular deflections of the energy in various directions constituting 'diffracted' pencils. We have met with and considered several illustrations of this effect. In all cases of this kind it is a necessity that there should be no great disparity between the length of the wave on the one hand, and that of the regular spacing or particle diameter on the other. Laue thought that previous failures to find diffraction in the case of X-rays might be due to a want of observance of this condition. If the X-ray wave-lengths were thousands of times shorter than those of light, as he had reason for believing, it was useless to look for diffraction effects with ordinary gratings in the ordinary way. One ought to employ gratings in which the lines were drawn thousands of times closer together than in the usual practice. This is not practicable: no one can draw millions of parallel lines to the inch.

It was possible, however, that Nature had already provided the tool which could not be constructed in the workshop. The crystal might be the appropriate grating for the X-rays, because its atoms were supposed to be in regular array, and the distances that separated them were, so far as could be calculated, of the same order as the wave-length of the X-ray. Whether these anticipations were well or ill founded, they became of little consequence when the experiment was made in 1912 by Laue's colleagues, Friedrich and Knipping, and was completely successful. A complicated but symmetrical pattern of spots appeared upon the photographic plate, which, though unlike any diffraction pattern due to light, was clearly of the same nature. It was soon found that every crystal produced its own pattern and that the experiment opened up not only a new method for the investigation of the nature of X-rays, but also a new means of analysis of the structure of crystals.

Examples of these patterns are given in Plate XXIIA,B They may be compared with Plate XXIIIc.

In order that these points may be clear it is necessary to examine, at not too great length, the details of the experiment and its implications. We have already examined certain phenomena of crystalline structure in the case of Iceland spar; but it will be convenient to reconsider the subject and to discuss it more generally.

The most striking and characteristic features of a crystal are its regularity of form, the polished evenness of its faces and the sharpness of its edges. If we compare crystals of the same composition we find that the angles between faces are always exactly the same from crystal to crystal: while the relative values of the areas of the faces may vary considerably. In technical terms, the faces of different specimens may be unequally developed. It is natural to infer that there is an underlying regularity of structure, involving the repetition in space of a unit which is too small to be visible. As a simple analogy we might take a piece of material woven, as is customary, with warp and weft at right angles to each other. However it might be torn, it would form pieces with right angles at all the corners: but the pieces would not necessarily be square. There would be two principal directions at right angles to each other: and all tears would take place at right angles to one or other of them. If the two directions were exactly alike, in all the characteristics that could be examined, if for example, they tore with equal ease, and if the frayed edges were the same on all sides, the warp and weft must be identical: they must be composed of the same threads and have the same spacings. We could rightly say that the material is founded on a 'square' pattern. This would still be the case even if both warp and weft were not simple but complex: if for example, each of them contained coloured threads at various intervals. So long as the scheme of repetition was the same in both we should still say the pattern was square: as for example a tartan might be.

The analogy of a woven material is insufficient to represent all the complications of a crystal structure; because warp and weft cannot be inclined to each other at any angle except ninety degrees: but it illustrates the important point that in any structure built of repetitions in space, the angles of the whole must be always the same, while no such restriction applies to the areas of the faces. The unit that is repeated in every direction determines the angular form. If, for example, the unit of a composition in a plane had the form of the small unit (Fig. 101), the whole might have various shapes such as are illustrated in the same figure. The edges need not always include the same angles as the edges of A but they would necessarily be inclined to one another at angles which from specimen to specimen would be invariable.

So also in the solid crystal various faces might be developed which would, in regard to the angles made with each other, display the same constancy of mutual inclination. As this is what we should expect if the crystal is composed of units repeated regularly in all directions, and as the facts agree with expectations, we assume that our preliminary conceptions of crystal structure are correct.

What will happen when a train of ether waves meets such a crystalline arrangement ?

A crystal can be thought of as a series of layers spaced at regular intervals, just as in two dimensions a regular assemblage of points can be thought of as a set of rows

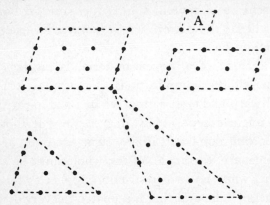

Fig. 101. The unit of a planar design is included in the outline A. The multiplication of the unit may assume various forms, a few of which are shown. The mutual inclinations of the edges are limited to certain definite angles.

equally spaced. Also, just as in the simpler case the rows might be made up in various ways as in Fig. 102, so also any one crystal can be divided up in an infinite number of ways into parallel sheets.

It is convenient to consider the problem of the diffraction of X-rays in stages: first taking the scattering by a single unit, then by a sheet of units, then by the whole crystal which is made up of a succession of sheets.

The unit in a crystal is made up of a certain number of atoms arranged in a certain way: the composition and arrangement vary from crystal to crystal. When the train of waves meets the unit each atom in it scatters and can be regarded as the centre of a series of ripples spreading outwards in spherical form. At a little distance these melt into one another, and in the end there is but one spherical wave having its centre somewhere within the unit. There is however this peculi-

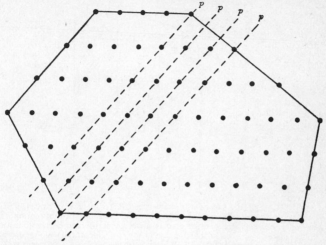

Fig. 102. The points in the figure can be arranged in rows in various ways.

arity about the wave, that it is not equally strong in all directions. To take a simple case, imagine the unit to consist of two atoms A and B, separated by a distance equal to half the length of a wave, as in Fig. 103. The oncoming waves arrive simultaneously at the two. The waves scattered by A and B start off together. In the direction ABC the two systems are always in opposition: a crest of one set fits into a hollow in the other. In this direction they destroy each other's effects. The same happens in the reverse direction BAD. But in every other direction there is no such complete interference: in a direction such as that marked by the arrow P they support each other to some extent, and more so as the direction P is separated from C or D. In this case the combination of the scattered waves will have a spherical form, but it will not be equally intense all

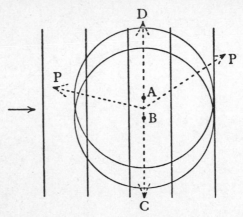

Fig. 103. Waves represented by the vertical lines are moving upon the two atoms A and B which scatter a small fraction of their energy. The two are half a wave-length distant from one another. The spherical waves that spread away annul one another in the directions A B C or B A D, because the crest of one fits into the hollow of the other. But energy is scattered in all other directions such as are indicated by the arrows marked P. This is really a particular case of Fig. 73.

round. There will be points C and D where the wave vanishes as the figure shows.

Other arrangements of the atoms lead to other distributions of intensity on the spherical surface: and the more complicated the arrangement the more complicated the distribution.

This complexity has however no effect on the development of our argument and is described only to make the picture more real. The one important point is that whatever the composition and arrangement of the unit,

all the units behave alike. As far as we are concerned
for the moment we may disregard the inequality of the
distribution of the energy on the surface of the scattered
wave, and remember only that the waves are in the end
spherical, and that they may be regarded as originating

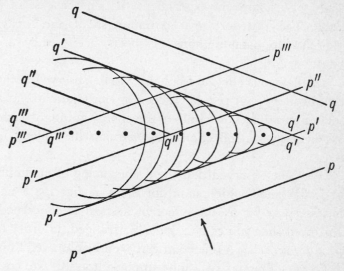

Fig. 104. Waves $p\,p$, $p'\,p'$ . . . . . sweep over a row of points where some
scattering takes place. The most of the energy goes on, but a fraction is
reflected in the form of waves $q\,q$, $q'\,q'$ . . . .

from regularly arranged points which represent the
positions of the units.

We now go on to consider the combined effect of the
units in a sheet. Suppose that the dots in Fig. 104
represent some of the units of pattern in a sheet which
is at right angles to the paper. A set of waves is shown
in section by the straight lines pp, $p'p'$, etc. As each
wave sweeps over the points, spherical waves spread
away from the point in turn, and a reflected wave is

formed by their combination. This is in fact another instance of the application of the Huygens principle. We have a case of simple reflection, differing only from reflection by a mirror in the fact that only a portion of the original energy is carried away by the reflected wave. We know by experiment that in the case of a single sheet this portion is extremely small: the X-rays often sweep over millions of sheets before they are finally spent.

An analogous effect is frequently to be observed in the case of sound. A regular reflection can take place at a set of iron railings, the bulk of the energy going through. We hear such a reflection when we pass the railings in a car.

It is to be observed that the even spacing of the units, and of the dots which stand for them in Fig. 104 is not necessary so far as the effect of a sheet is concerned. Nor need the railings be regularly arranged, in order to produce an echo: a reflection can even be observed from a hedge. Regularity is not important until we consider the possibility of reflection by many different sets of planes within the crystal.

In the diagram Fig. 105 we represent a section of these sheets by the lines S_1 S_2 S_3, and so on; we draw them as full lines and not as rows of dots because it is of no importance where the units or the representative dots lie in each sheet. For convenience also we show by straight lines the directions in which the waves are travelling instead of the waves themselves. Thus aPa_1 represents a case of reflection in a single sheet which we have just been considering. Besides the set represented by aPa_1 there is another case of reflection represented by bQb_1, another by cRc_1, and so on. The dimensions of the figure are grossly exaggerated in certain directions so as to show the argument more clearly. The distances between the layers are in actuality minute compared to the width of the pencil. Each ray, like bQb_1 represents a train of

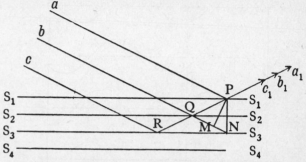

Fig. 105. The diagram illustrates the reflection of a train of waves by a series of regular spaced sheets, each capable of reflecting a small fraction of the energy of the train.

waves moving on so broad a front that the various reflected trains overlap one another sideways.

The reflected set represented by bQb_1 has had further to go than aPa_1, before it re-appears and joins the latter. If we draw perpendicular distances PM and PN the extra distance is MN.

And again the set cRc_1 lags behind bQb_1 just as much again as this lags behind aPa_1, because the sheets are spaced at even distances. Behind this other reflections follow at regular intervals. The wave reflected by the crystal is the sum of all these. We may represent the summation by Fig. 106 in which curves representing the reflected sets of waves are put one below another: each lagging behind the one above it by the distance

MN. These waves are to be added up; for instance, along the vertical line shown in Fig. 106 we are to add together O*a*, O*b*, O*c*, etc., giving positive signs to those that are above the horizontal line and negative to those that are below. Usually the sum of those quantities will

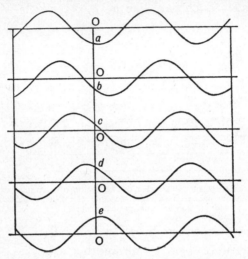

Fig. 106. A diagram to show how the reflected waves of Fig. 105 add up to nothing unless they are all exactly in phase with one another. The quantity o *a* + o *b* + o *c* + ... is zero because there are as many positive as negative terms in the millions that must be added together. The exception is when the reflections are all in phase, the crests of one set being exactly above or below (in this kind of figure) crests of all the other sets.

be zero, because they are just as likely to be above as below the line, and in their millions every possible size up to a maximum is to be found. The meaning of this is that there is no reflected pencil: its constituents have destroyed one another. There is one exception to this rule. If the lag is exactly one wave-length or two, or three, or any whole number of wave-lengths, so that the curves shown in Fig. 106 lie exactly below one another, then the sum of them all is just a multiple of one of them, and as the multiplier is large the reflection is large also. The reflected energy cannot of course be greater than the incident, but calculation shows that over a very small range on either side of the reflecting angle the reflection is complete.

The amount of the lag depends on two things, the angle at which the rays strike the crystal and the spacing of the sheets. If they are nearly perpendicular to the sheets, the lag is twice the distance between two sheets that are neighbours: and this is its maximum value. The more oblique the incidence the smaller the lag; at glancing incidence it becomes very small. Thus provided the wave-length is not too great there must always be some particular angle of incidence at which the lag is exactly one wave-length or even more wavelengths: and at these angles the reflection leaps out strongly.

If our primary rays are of one wave-length we must turn the crystal round until the angle is right. If the angle of incidence has a fixed value we may get a reflection by throwing a mixed beam upon the crystal, out of which rays of the right wave-length will be selected for reflection while the rest pass on. The late Lord Rayleigh once showed at a lecture in the Royal Institution an analogous experiment in acoustics. As its dimensions are on a scale so much larger than those of X-rays and crystals, it helps to an appreciation of the latter case. Sound waves are produced by a whistle of very high pitch, known as a bird-call. The waves are only an inch or so in length, much shorter than the waves of ordinary speech, but hundreds of millions of times longer than the ether waves of X-rays. The note is so high that many ears, especially those of older people cannot perceive it. A set of muslin screens, about a foot square are arranged in parallel sequence, upon a system of lazy-tongs which allows the common spacing to be varied. The screens may for our purpose be taken to correspond to the sheets of Fig. 105: each can reflect a small fraction of an incident sound wave, but allows the bulk of it to go on.

If now the whistle and the set of screens is arranged as in the photograph, Plate XXIIc, the sound may be reflected by the screen. The reflected sound, if it exists, is very easily detected by means of the 'sensitive flame.' This is a luminous gas jet issuing under great pressure from a long narrow tube with a fine nozzle. The pressure is adjusted until the flame is on the point of flaring, under which circumstances a high pitched sound causes it to duck and flare in a most striking way. The rapid alternations of pressure in the sound wave are the direct cause of the effect. The sensitive flame is so placed that it can detect the reflected sound if there is any, but it is screened from any direct action of the bird-call.

It is then found that if, by means of the lazy-tongs, the common spacing of the screens is altered gradually and continuously the flame passes through successive phases of flaring and silence. The explanation is the same as that of the X-ray effect just described. If there is flaring it means that the reflections from the successive screens all conspire, and this happens if the spacing is so adjusted that the lag of one reflection behind another is a whole number of wave-lengths.

PLATE XXII

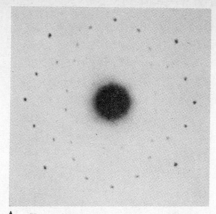

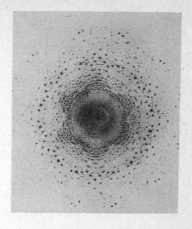

A. X-ray diffraction spectrum of rocksalt.
(*p. 236*)

B. An X-ray diffraction spectrum of kaliophilite. (*p. 236*)

Bannister

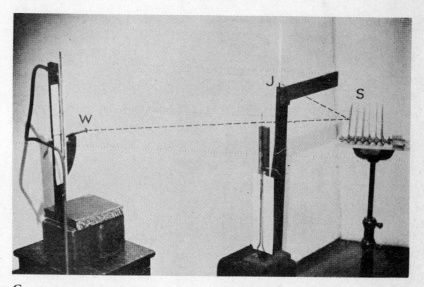

C. A photograph of the apparatus used by Lord Rayleigh and described on pp. 245-6. The whistle is at W, the set of screens at S, and the luminous gas jet at J. The dotted lines show roughly the course of the sound waves that affect the jet. The photograph shows the appearance of the jet when there is no sound, or when the screens (seen edgeways in the picture) are not placed so that their reflections reinforce one another. Owing to a peculiarity in the form of the nozzle at J, the jet does not respond to sound proceeding directly from W to J. When the screens are properly spaced the jet broadens and ducks to a fraction of its normal height.

PLATE XXIII

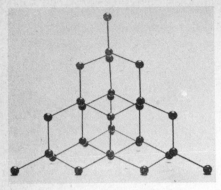

A. A model showing the structure of diamond. Each ball represents a carbon atom in respect to position only, but not in respect to form or size. The distance between the centres of two neighbouring atoms is 1.54 Angstrom Units · (One unit is the hundred-millionth of a centimetre.) (*p.* 249)

B. The arrangement of the molecules in a crystal of stearic acid. Each zig-zag represents the carbon atoms of a single molecule. The distance between the centres of two neighbouring carbon atoms is 1.54 Angstrom Units, as in diamond. The two models A and B are built on different scales. The terminal groups and the hydrogens are not shown. (From a diagram due to A. Muller, Davy Faraday Laboratory). (*p.* 249)

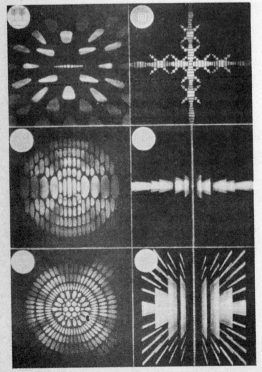

C. A set of optical diffraction spectra, due to Fraunhöfer — from Guillemin's *Forces of Nature*. The light is diffracted in each case by a screen containing a regular arrangement of fine openings, e.g. a part of a feather. The original is coloured, but the differences in colour are not shown in this reproduction. These optical spectra may be compared with the X-ray spectra of XXII A, B. (*p.* 236)

Rayleigh used the analogy for the purpose of explaining the brilliant colours of crystals of chlorate of potash. These crystals have a peculiar formation, being composed of alternating layers of the crystalline material differing only in the orientation of their crystalline axes. The thickness of the layer is thousands of times smaller than the spacing of the muslin screen, but again thousands of times larger than the spacings of the layers in which the crystalline units are disposed. It is of the order of the wavelength of visible light. The same argument holds in all three cases.

We have one more point to consider before we can appreciate Laue's experiment.

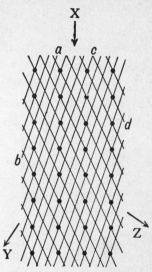

Fig. 107. The dots represent the units of a cubic crystal. The scale would be about 100,000,000 to one. The direction marked x is that of the incident X-rays. There are reflections in the direction y due to planes parallel to $a\ b$, and in the direction z due to planes parallel to $c\ d$; also in other directions not indicated.

We have to remember that there is not only one way, there are an infinite number of ways in which a crystal can be divided into parallel sheets. Suppose that Fig. 107 represents for example the disposition of the units in a cubic crystal: a section by the plane of the paper is all that can conveniently be shown in such a diagram. We may consider the division into sheets to be made parallel to $a\ b$ and as far as this set of sheets is concerned, there will be a partial reflection of X-rays. Out of the original pencil which must contain a variety of wave-lengths a sharply defined selection will be reflected in the direction Y consisting of those for which the lag is equal to the wave-length: the lag depends as already said on the spacing and on the angle of incidence.

The crystal can also be divided into sheets which cut the plane of the diagram in lines parallel to *c d*. In this case reflection takes place at a different angle, and the rays reflected are of a different wave-length. The reflected ray moves away in the direction Z and makes another spot on the photographic plate.

Thus many reflections occur simultaneously and make their impressions on the photographic plate. If the crystal is of a cubic design and the incident rays are parallel to one edge the pattern that is formed will be symmetrical about two straight lines at right angles as in Plate XXIIA. If, on the other hand, the crystal is of a hexagonal design we have a six-sided figure as in Plate XXIIB. All these agreements between observed results and calculated expectations are perfect, and it is obvious that the fundamental hypothesis is correct. The X-rays have as much right to be spoken of as ether waves as light itself.

The two illustrations of Laue photographs (Plate XXII) differ much from each other: their difference illustrates the remarkable diversity that is found in such photographs. Every crystal writes its own signature. It is in some cases easy to deduce the structure of the crystal from the picture which is characteristic of it. In others the task is accomplished with difficulty: in a still greater number of cases the solution is more than present technique and skill can accomplish. Since every solid substance contains parts that are crystalline, and since in many of them the whole is an aggregation of crystals, it will readily be understood that a knowledge of crystal structure often affords an explanation of the properties of the substance. One or two examples are given in Plate XXIIIA,B, but it would be out of place to consider this subject in detail, and indeed impossible, for it has grown so rapidly that a considerable treatise is now required to give any reasonable account of it. We must be content with the proof that the X-rays can be considered as ether waves.

It is easy to include in the same list certain rays which are emitted by radio-active substances. These are known as gamma rays. Soon after the first developments that followed on Laue's experiment it was shown that gamma rays could be reflected by a crystal of rock salt in exactly the same manner. If the X-rays are ether waves, the gamma rays must be ether waves also. They have greater penetrating powers than X-rays, being able to pass through inches of lead and yet to retain an appreciable fraction of their original strength.

At the other end of the scale are the ether waves used in broadcasting. These are produced by electric machinery. The proof that they are of the same nature as light was given by Clerk Maxwell when he calculated the velocity of such waves and found it to be the same as that of light. And since then the assumption that light is an electromagnetic disturbance has led to many calculations which have been verified by experiment

To sum up, therefore, we find that we can observe ether waves of widely differing lengths. We begin with the great waves used in radio work, hundreds of metres in length: these are produced electrically. By reducing the dimensions of the electrical generators we can correspondingly reduce the length of wave, and in this way it has been found possible to work with waves two or three centimetres in length. Below this is an awkward gap to fill for technical reasons, but we pick up the thread again when we come to the vibrations known as the infra-red, where the wave-lengths are a few ten-thousandths of a centimetre. Then comes the visible range of which naturally we know so much more than we do of the rest: it is very narrow, for the extreme red has a wave-length of somewhat less than one ten-thousandth of a centimetre and the extreme blue about half so much. The whole is confined, we may say, within one octave. The ultra-violet comes next, by which term we generally mean the wave-lengths that are just outside the visible and range up to an indefinite value, let us say to the hundred thousandth of a centimetre. Then follows a difficult region where the rays are highly absorbed by the atmosphere and all work must be carried on in a vacuum. It has been difficult to bridge across this gap and reach the X-rays on the further side: the task has been successfully accomplished however in recent years. In the X-ray region experimental work becomes easy again, thanks to the new methods of the crystal grating: and so we pass on to the gamma rays of increasing penetration, and finally it may be to the 'cosmic' rays which are said to come from space, are extremely penetrating, and

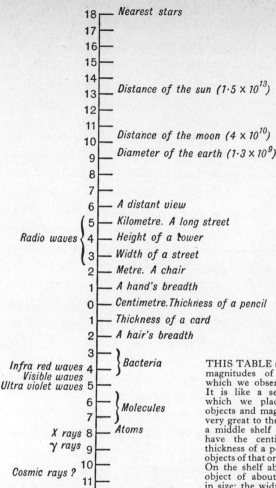

18	Nearest stars
17	
16	
15	
14	
13	Distance of the sun $(1 \cdot 5 \times 10^{13})$
12	
11	
10	Distance of the moon (4×10^{10})
9	Diameter of the earth $(1 \cdot 3 \times 10^{9})$
8	
7	
6	A distant view
5	Kilometre. A long street
4	Height of a tower
3	Width of a street
2	Metre. A chair
1	A hand's breadth
0	Centimetre. Thickness of a pencil
1	Thickness of a card
2	A hair's breadth

Radio waves { 5, 4, 3

Infra red waves — 4 } Bacteria
Visible waves
Ultra violet waves — 5

6 } Molecules
7

X rays — 8 Atoms
γ rays — 9

Cosmic rays? — 10

11
12
13 Atomic nuclei
14

THIS TABLE shows the relative magnitudes of various objects which we observe and measure. It is like a set of shelves on which we place specimens of objects and magnitudes from the very great to the very small. On a middle shelf marked zero, we have the centimetre, and the thickness of a pencil to represent objects of that order of magnitude. On the shelf above we place an object of about ten centimetres in size; the width of a hand will serve. The shelf above takes objects of about a hundred centimetres, for example smaller objects of furniture. The width of a street will represent the thousand centimetres, the height of a tower might be ten thousand centimetres or a hundred metres, and so on. Below the zero shelf comes first a shelf holding something of the order of a millimetre in thickness, as a card; then the hair's breadth on the next shelf and so on. Bacteria are at various heights on the third and fourth shelves down; molecules on the sixth and seventh, atoms nearly down to the eighth. On the other side of the vertical line the various wave-lengths are shown in the same way. Distances are sometimes given in figures. The sun's distance is fifteen million million centimetres or in symbols 1.5×10^{13}. This goes therefore on the thirteenth shelf up.

appear to be akin to gamma rays. It may be convenient to set out these magnitudes in a table: and at the same time to add a few other magnitudes for comparison.

This short survey of the range of ether waves may be concluded by a few words of description of the methods by which the wave-lengths are measured. Most of them depend on the use of the diffraction grating, as explained on p. 135. If a ray of light falls perpendicularly upon a grating as illustrated in Fig. 69 the diffracted pencils pass off to right and to left: and the angle which these pencils make with the original direction of the ray depends upon the ratio between the wave-length and the distance of repeat of the grating. When a grating is prepared in the ruling machine, the number of lines to the centimetre is a matter of the arrangement of the working parts of the machine and is known. As soon, therefore, as the angle has been observed the calculation of wave-length is an easy matter.

The grating method can be applied to infra-red and ultra-violet also. It can even be applied to the X-rays but this has been accomplished only recently. The first measurements of X-ray wave-lengths were based on the use of the crystal as a diffraction grating. As soon as the structures of simple crystals like rock salt or calcite were known, it became possible to calculate the distance of repeat in the crystal pattern. The weights of the atoms are known with fair precision from chemical and physical considerations. In rock salt for example, the atoms are arranged in straight rows: the weight of a cubic centimetre of the crystal is known, and the weights of atoms of sodium and chlorine are known also: from these figures the spacings of the crystal can be calculated. When the reflection of a pencil of X-rays by a crystal is observed (see Fig. 105), and the angle of reflection noted, the wave-length of the X-ray becomes known. Fuller accounts of these measurements are given in books which describe the new methods.

More recently the diffraction of X-rays by ordinary gratings has been observed. It is necessary that the incidence should be very oblique, since there is so great a difference between wave-length and the spacing of an artificial grating. It will be remembered that such a diffraction experiment seemed at one time to be too difficult to attempt, for which reason Laue proposed the use of the crystal. Naturally however the proof that the X-ray was entirely akin to light and the importance of the measurement encouraged the further attempt which succeeded. It is possible that this new way is more accurate than that which made use of the crystal. It is certainly more direct. It is worth observing that by means of the crystal methods, the wave-lengths of X-rays can be compared with each other, and the spacings of crystals with each other far more accurately than either can be compared with the standards of lengths.

The wave-lengths of gamma rays may also be found with the aid of the crystal. There remain only the long waves of radio, and these are known by observations of frequency, that is of the number of vibrations per second. The general velocity of ether waves is known, and therefore the frequency gives the length.

CHAPTER IX

THE WAVE AND THE CORPUSCLE

IN the preceding chapter we have seen that a wide range of ether waves is at our disposal for experiment. Certain of them which lie within a narrow range are visible to our eyes: others may be detected by their action on a photographic plate. The very long radio waves are perceived by the aid of a combination of electric devices known as a wireless set. We shall have occasion to consider other methods of detection in what follows.

The characteristic phenomena which have induced us to consider visible light as a form of wave motion in the ether are displayed throughout the whole range of the radiations: especially the phenomena of diffraction, of which we have made much use. It is to be expected that any other phenomena which we may find to be displayed by one quality of radiation will be displayed more or less by the rest.

There is one particular phenomenon which is shown markedly by the radiations of the shortest wave-lengths, and to a less observable extent by the longer waves: it is known as the photo-electric effect. At this point the wave theory which has helped us so far fails to suggest an explanation. It is this fact and others associated with it that show our wave hypothesis to be incomplete, and lead to the curious position of physics at the present

254

Fig. 108. This figure like those of Figs. 96, 97, 98 and 99 is from a block used to illustrate the lecture given by Crookes at the Royal Institution in 1879. The glass is blown into the form of a bulb; the negative pole or cathode is at the bottom: there is an anode or positive pole at the top but its position is immaterial. The target is a piece of platinum wire *b*: which might also have served as the anode. The cup-shaped cathode concentrates the stream upon the target. As Crookes described it, 'The platinum wire not only gets white hot, but you can see the sparks coming from it on all sides, showing that it is actually melting.' The experiment was arranged to illustrate the development of heat, it was not known then nor for twenty years afterwards that the platinum was radiating X-rays. The bulb in the figure is about six inches high.

time. In 1905 Einstein suggested that the corpuscular theory had been set aside too hastily.

The Photo-electric Effect

The photo-electric effect is easily described. When light strikes any material substance it causes the atoms of the substance to emit electrons, whence the name: since X-rays and gamma rays are also to be classed as forms of light the name is made to cover the effect in their case also. And since the emission of electrons is in their case a very notable occurrence, easily observed and easily measured, it is simpler to investigate the effect with the aid of these shorter wavelengths. It is to be observed that the effect is continuously manifested as we pass from one wave-length to another: it is only because it is so much more easily investigated by means of the short waves that we use them in preference to the visible rays which were known to show the property before X-rays were discovered.

Perhaps the easiest way of obtaining a general view of the phenomenon is to begin with the production of the X-rays in the X-ray bulb, and afterwards to follow them as they make their way outside.

The elements of the X-ray tube or bulb are (*a*) the containing bulb itself, which is made at least in part of glass and (*b*) the two metal conductors, the cathode, and the anode or anti-cathode or target or positive terminal. We have already observed some of the phenomena which attend the discharge of electricity through such a tube when it has been largely exhausted of air. A stream of electrons is ejected from the cathode like water from a jet. It moves in a straight line, but can be deflected by a magnet: it has mechanical effects, and it heats wherever it strikes. Also X-rays radiate from the place of impact wherever that may be. The cathode ray stream pays no attention to the position of the positive terminal; if the target is used as the positive it must be put in the right place when the tube is being made, so that the electron stream may strike it. The positive terminal has the appearance of being idle, but this cannot be so in reality because it is wanted to complete the electric circuit. It must impart the positive electricity to the atoms and molecules that are to carry it; these, being relatively massive do not acquire the self-revealing speed of the electrons in the cathode stream. The confinement of the stream within definite bounds and the directness with which it leaves the cathode and makes its way across the tube are most remarkable. When there is a little gas in the tube the stream is visible because of the collisions between the flying electrons and the gas molecules. The track of the stream is then a fine luminous pencil. Experience shows that its form is largely influenced by the shape of the tube and the cathode; more immediately by the action of the electric charges which accumulate on the walls of the tube.

Crookes supposed that the stream consisted of radiant matter projected from the cathode.

He had to fight for his idea, because it appeared that if it struck a thin place in the tube wall, it could penetrate and emerge into the open air, being faintly visible in a darkened room. The same penetration could be observed when very thin screens were placed in the path of the rays within the tube. Consequently, it was argued, the rays could not be due to particles carrying electric charges, as Crookes imagined, but must be some sort of wave. At that time it was not thought possible for particles of any sort to go in straight lines through material sheets however thin. Crookes was perfectly correct however, and was completely justified when J. J. Thomson showed that the stream consisted of negatively charged 'corpuscles,' to use his first designation, or electrons as they were named subsequently. Thomson was able to measure the charge of the electron, and its mass, and showed that under all circumstances and for every kind of X-ray tube the charge and mass were the same. The mass was very small: the hydrogen atom, believed until then to be the smallest particle in the world, was 1,845 times as big. The universality of the electron showed it to be a fundamental constituent of all atoms: as is well known now, the normal atom can be described as consisting of a positive nucleus and a sufficient number of electrons to counterbalance the positive nuclear charge.

The speed of the electron, as it shot away from the cathode, was determined by electrical and magnetic methods, and it appeared, as one might expect, that the greater the electric power applied to the tube the swifter the flight of the electron. To be more exact it is necessary to use technical terms: a potential of 10 volts produced a speed of one hundredth of the velocity of light: 1,000 volts nearly one tenth: and at 100,000 volts the speed was not far short of that of light itself. Yet, however great was the applied potential, the speed never exceeded the velocity of light: it approached a final value more and more slowly as the potential was raised.

The modern X-ray tube is a very carefully designed instrument (Plate XXIV). The essential parts remain the same, but experience has shown how important is design if good results are to be obtained. Into these details we need not go.

We have next to consider how the X-rays originate. It was Röntgen who first discovered their existence, as explained already, and showed that they came from the spot where the cathode ray stream hit the wall of the tube or any target placed to receive them. The energy of the cathode ray stream is in part converted into the energy of the X-rays. By far the greater part of the energy of the stream is converted into heat at the place where the rays strike: and in any but the very weakest tubes the heat developed is such that the glass wall of

PLATE XXIV

A machine for producing X-rays of relatively large wave length in great quantity for the purpose of crystal analysis. The target is a mass of steel weighing 2 cwt. and revolving 2,000 times a minute. By means of this motion, and by water cooling, the heat generated by the impact of the cathode rays is dissipated. The target is within the cylinder resting on the left of the lathe-bed. The motor which drives the target is on the right of the bed. The rays pass through the long narrow tube on the left to the crystal holder in the bottom left hand corner. The reflected rays are received by a camera mounted on slides; it stands a little below the middle of the picture. (p. 258)

the tube is quickly punctured if the current is left running. It is usual to provide a solid and massive target, of some metal of high atomic weight such as platinum or tungsten. Even this may become red hot unless a water cooling device is included in the design of the tube. We now picture to ourselves the X-rays, whatever they may be, streaming away from the place where the electrons strike the target. The photographic plate is used to find their direction and intensity. It is quickly found, as already stated, that they move in straight lines, and have the power of penetrating – still moving in straight lines – any material on which they fall. It also appears that their penetrating power varies greatly according to the conditions under which they are generated. The faster the electrons in the cathode ray stream, the more penetrating are the X-rays which the electrons produce. The quality depends also to a certain extent on the nature of the target which the electrons strike. The higher the atomic weight the greater the proportion of penetrating X-rays in the general complex; though to produce penetrating X-rays from any target the electrons must be sufficiently swift. The target in the X-ray tube employed for medical purposes is usually made of tungsten: in the special case of crystal analysis, it is more common to use copper or iron because a 'soft' or less penetrating radiation is required.

Penetration is the property to which attention is paid by workers who use X-rays for various practical purposes, including those of medicine and surgery. To take a simple case, rays that are too 'soft,' that is to say have too little power of penetration, do not provide the surgeon with a useful picture of a broken limb. The rays cannot penetrate the flesh sufficiently well, and when the photographic plate is placed beneath the limb to receive the rays, the flesh casts almost as deep a shadow as the bone. When a higher potential, that is to say more volts, are applied to the tube, the velocity of the electrons increases, and the rays become more penetrating: the flesh ceases to cast a strong shadow, but the bones which contain calcium and other heavy atoms still absorb the rays so well that a shadow which is bold and easily discernible lies within the lighter shadow of the flesh. If the voltage is too high, even the bones may cease to intercept the rays sufficiently and their shadows become weak also.

It is readily shown by the methods of crystal analysis that the penetration of the X-ray depends directly upon its wave-length. The effect of increasing the velocity of the originating electrons is to shorten the wave-length of the X-rays to which they give rise. If the intensity of the cathode stream is increased, that is to say, the number of electrons which strike the target in a second, the intensity of the X-rays increases also. A photographic plate which is exposed to them blackens more quickly. The quality of the X-rays, in other words their wave-length, does not depend at all upon the number of electrons in the cathode stream, but on their velocity only. The number of electrons determines intensity, speed determines wave-length.

Now we come to the photo-electric effect. The X-rays cause the ejection of electrons from any body on which they fall. It is in doing this that they spend their energy. The effect is not upon the body as a whole but upon the separate atoms of which the body is composed. The rays treat, so to speak, with the atoms individually and do not pay any attention to the way in which the atoms are assembled into molecules or the molecules into the solid. An X-ray stream flowing past a given atom has a certain chance of acting upon that atom and causing the ejection of an electron. It is an extremely small chance in any case; the energy of the rays would be very quickly used up if they were successful with every atom over which they passed. There are millions of millions of failures to one success. But whatever the magnitude of the chance, it is not altered by any attachment of the atom to other atoms. Of course this cannot be true of all wave-lengths; we are indeed familiar with the fact that the absorption of light waves depends very much indeed on chemical composition. But in the case of X-rays the effect is at least negligible. A few examples of the effects of chemical composition have been found, but they are rare and so small that their observation is difficult.

If we include within the term 'ejection' cases where the action of the X-ray upon the atom causes the shifting of an electron from its proper place within the atom to some other place within the same atom, so that the ejection is incomplete, we describe, practically in full, the action of the X-ray. It has no other effect on material substances, and manifests its presence in no other way. Just as the moving electrons in the X-ray tube originated the X-rays, so now the X-rays start electrons into motion. When the X-rays fall upon the silver salts on the photographic plate they start electrons into activity, and it is they that cause the chemical action which forms the essential process of the plate. When they penetrate the human body, the action upon the body tissues is due to the electrons which are set in motion. It is as if the body was subjected to the action of explosive shells.

It becomes a matter of great interest to enquire what sort of velocity these electrons possess that are ejected by atoms under the influence of the X-rays. Long ago various attempts were made to answer this question. One of the first was due to Innes in 1907. The method was simple, and it is easy to describe. The X-rays strike a plate of some material MM and electrons are ejected from it in all directions. Two screens L and L' are pierced with small holes at Q and R. The electrons that go through the holes strike a photographic plate at P, and RQP is a straight line. The diagram (Fig. 109) gives an indication of the arrangements of plates and screens, but does not show all the usual details required when sensitive plates are used.

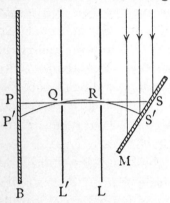

Fig. 109. A diagram showing the essential principle of Innes's experiment.

Now a stream of electrons in flight can be bent aside by a magnet as we have already seen, in fact the path becomes circular and the stream tends to return into itself. The amount of bending depends on the strength of the magnet on the one hand, and on the charge, velocity, and mass of the carriers of the electricity on the other. When Innes carried out his experiment the charge and mass of the electron had been measured by J. J. Thomson; and it was rightly assumed that electrons were the carriers in this case. Innes brought a magnet up to a determined position near his apparatus. The stream of electrons which now registered its effect upon the photographic plate was not that which went in the straight line, but a curved stream S'RQP', forming an arc of a circle. By observing the relative positions of Q, R, and P', it was possible for Innes to find the radius of the circle. He knew the strength of his magnet and could then calculate the one quantity which remained unknown, viz. the velocity of the electron.

A result of first class importance emerged from these observations. It was found that the electrons were moving with a high speed, which was comparable with that of the electrons in the bulb where the X-rays were generated. The speed did not depend upon the intensity of the X-rays: a fact which was easily established by repeating the experiment when the distance of the bulb from the plate MM was varied. Even when the bulb's distance was increased eight times so that the intensity of the rays falling upon the plate was diminished sixty-four times, according to the law of the inverse square, there was no change in the position of the spot P'. A longer exposure was of course required to obtain a visible effect upon the plate: but this would naturally follow upon the diminution of the number of electrons in the stream. The number of electrons was less, but their velocity was unchanged.

On the other hand, it appeared that when the electrons in the X-ray bulb were made to move faster, and the X-rays therefore became more penetrating, the electron stream in the experiment also became more rapid.

Change in the nature of the plate MM made some difference, but it was not great. Raising the atomic weight, as for instance replacing silver by gold, caused the appearance of some rather faster electrons in the general complex. The speeds in fact lay within a certain range, the fastest exceeding the slowest speed by about 20 %: and while the lower limit remained the same the upper was somewhat raised. Compared with the other observations this, as was surmised then, and as we now know, was only a secondary effect.

The observations made by Innes were confirmed and extended by other workers.

Thus the whole combined phenomenon presents a comparatively simple aspect. It begins when electrons are shot at a target in the X-ray tube with, let us say, a definite velocity, although in practice it is difficult to confine that velocity within very narrow limits. In the intermediate stage, there is a transference of energy by the agency of the X-rays through the walls of the tube into space outside. In the end electrons appear, moving with velocities of the same order – as a matter of fact not quite so great – as the original electrons. It is as if a stream had disappeared underground and reappeared somewhere else: only we cannot of course assume that the same electrons are in evidence in each case. We cannot mark them as we might colour the water of the stream. The materials of the tube and of the plate MM, and the disposition of the experiment, are of little or no consequence. We begin with electrons moving with a certain velocity in one place, and we end with electrons moving with nearly the same velocity in another place.

It is convenient to imagine a great enlargement of the whole process, as in this way we get an idea of the relative magnitudes of electrons and atoms and of the dimensions of the experiment. Suppose that the target in the X-ray tube is magnified a hundred million times and becomes comparable with the moon. The electrons with which it is bombarded are still too small to be seen by the naked eye. The distance of the moon from the earth will now correspond roughly to the distance which separates the X-ray bulb from the observer under ordinary conditions. An atom is then about the size of a cherry or a plum. The moon is peppered with the extremely fine invisible corpuscles representing the electrons. Immediately similar corpuscles begin to jump out of the earth in various places: one, let us say, out of a stone lying on the top of a mountain in the Andes, the next out of a drop of water in the Indian Ocean, the next out of a leaf in an English wood, and so on. The successive events are remarkably isolated from one another. And whatever may be the speed of the corpuscles that are fired at the moon, these secondary corpuscles possess similar speeds, which vary with those of the primary.

It is clear that it is beyond the capacity of the wave

theory, as we have pictured it, to include these strange phenomena as ordinary characteristics of wave motion. The essential difficulty lies in the explanation of the transference of energy from the one place to the other. For we cannot but assume such a transference. We might at first sight suppose that the energy of the electron which leaps out of the atom when the X-ray falls upon it comes from the atom itself, and that the X-ray does no more than prompt the atom to action, as when we pull the trigger of a gun. But if this were so we should expect every atom to shoot off its projectile with its own characteristic velocity, whereas we find that the velocity of the secondary electron is independent of the nature of the atom from which it springs. It depends rather on the quality of the prompting X-ray. and it is impossible to conceive of the velocity of the shot from a gun as depending on the quality of the man who pulls the trigger.

The unsatisfactory nature of the 'trigger' hypothesis is intensified when we consider an experiment of a different kind which can be performed with the rays from radioactive substances. These radiations are of three kinds, alpha, beta and gamma. The first of these consists of streams of helium atoms, which do not concern us here: the second consists of electrons moving at very high speed, higher in general than that of the electrons in the X-ray tube. The third consists of radiations of the same nature as light and X-rays, as we have seen already; they are more penetrating than X-rays, and bear much the same relation to the beta rays that X-rays do to the electrons to which they are due. When gamma rays pass over atoms, a very minute proportion of the latter emit electrons which have much the same velocity as the beta rays which are emitted by the radioactive substance, which emits beta rays and gamma rays at the same time. The whole process, in this case, has obvious parallels with the interaction between electrons and X-rays: it is in fact the same process on a different scale. Whatever holds for the one case must hold to some extent for the other.

Now experiments, which need not be described in detail, show that when gamma rays excite a beta, the latter does not leave the atom in any chance direction, but continues more or less in the direction of the gamma ray. Such a result is difficult to understand on any trigger theory: how could we imagine that if a man runs up to a gun and pulls the trigger, using no other force, the direction of the shot will bear any relation to the direction from which the man came?

The trigger hypothesis must be abandoned. The X-rays in some way bring to the atom the energy which is imparted to the emitted electron. How can we suppose this to be done?

As an X-ray, considered as a wave, spreads in a widening circle from its origin, its energy is spread thinner and thinner on the spherical surface. Yet we have seen that the speed with which the electron is emitted is independent of the intensity of the X-rays. Shall we suppose that the energy has to be stored up in each atom until it reaches a certain amount when there is a kind of explosion? But it would take a very long time, as calculation easily shows, to accumulate the energy. An atom is a very small object compared to the size of the widening sphere on which the wave energy lies: it can abstract so slowly that it would take longer than the lifetime of an ordinary X-ray bulb to collect a sufficient amount. Yet the X-rays are effective the moment the X-rays are turned on. Moreover it would again be difficult to understand why the velocity of the ejected electron has nothing to do with the atom from whence it comes, but depends on the velocity of the electron in the original stream. We may see the difficulty more clearly if we again imagine an example on a larger scale. Suppose we drop a plank into the sea from a given height, say 100 ft.: there is a splash and waves spread away over the surface of the water. They pass by boats and ships without any effect, and then after travelling thousands of miles they find a ship on which their effect is disastrous: a plank is torn out of the ship's side and hurled, ninety feet into the air, or fifty feet, or twenty, all such numbers seem equally ridiculous. Yet this is a fair parallel to any explanation of the photo-electric effect on the simple wave theory.

There is only one way out of the difficulty; it is quite simple and direct; and it meets all the experimental facts which we have just been considering. In order to bind the facts together we must use as our theory the conception of the X-ray as something corpuscular which picks up the energy of the electron in the X-ray tube at the moment and the place where it strikes some atom in the target. It moves off as a definite entity. It has powers which enable it to penetrate the glass of the bulb and other substances, but in the end one of its innumerable encounters with atoms reverses the process which gave it birth, its energy is transferred to an electron which moves off in the manner observed under experiment. It cannot matter much what atom brings about either the first change or the second: and the speed of the second electron may well be equal to, or approach in some measure, the velocity of the first. There may well be relations between the direction of motion of the X-ray, or gamma ray, and of the electrons which originate them or are originated by them.

This is a corpuscular theory: we have therefore come to the point where we find phenomena which suggest the use of the corpuscle, rather than that of the wave which has hitherto served us so well.

But what sort of corpuscle shall we suggest as capable of performing these duties? Many years ago (*Philosophical Magazine*, October 1907 *et sqq.*) I suggested that it might be a combination of an electron with some positive mass bearing a compensating electric charge, a 'neutral pair.' Such a pair being without charge might be expected to penetrate matter with an ease impossible to either of its constituents alone, since its electric and magnetic forces would be confined within very narrow limits. I then supposed that the pair might be made up from the two corpuscular radiations of radioactive substances; it might consist of one electron and one positively charged atom of helium. The suggestion seemed the less unlikely because it had not then been clearly shown that the X-rays were of the same character as light. But when it became clear that the X-rays were as much of the nature of waves as light, and light as corpuscular as X-rays seemed to be, it was no longer possible to regard light and X-rays as the distinct phenomena which the neutral pair hypothesis implied.

The packet of energy which takes the place of Newton's corpuscle is now called the photon. Light of all wavelengths, X-rays, infra-red rays and so on, can be considered as taking the form of a stream of photons. The idea of a neutron is not however entirely done away with, as evidence has recently been put forward of its existence in the form of a close combination of one electron, and one positively charged element or proton.

By a most ingenious device C. T. R. Wilson was able, in 1911, to confirm in a novel fashion the experimental results and the deductions therefrom which have just been described. His method provided an ocular demonstration which was convincing. The method turns upon certain physical effects which may require a brief explanation.

In the first place it must be observed that an electron moving through a gas is able to remove electrons from some of the atoms through which, or near which, it passes. Its speed must exceed a certain limit, about a hundred million centimetres per second, if it is to possess this power: indeed, if it has a lower speed it can make no way through the gas but apparently is held up and absorbed by almost the first atom it encounters. An electron set in motion by an X-ray may start off with ten to a hundred times this speed, an electron set in motion by a gamma ray possesses a still greater velocity.

The path of the first through air or any gas at ordinary temperature and pressure may be reckoned in millimetres or centimetres, that of the latter in metres. The track in either case, short or long, is marked by atoms from which electrons have been separated, and other atoms to which the removed electrons have temporarily attached themselves. There are therefore both positively charged and negatively charged atoms lying along the path which the electron has taken. Recombination at once sets in, the atoms with superfluous electrons restoring them to those which have been deprived: but for a few seconds or minutes both kinds persist.

The second feature of this beautiful experiment is the use which is made of a well known effect. When a gas is allowed to expand, it becomes colder: it has to spend energy in the process and so must draw on its store of heat. If the gas contains moisture there is a tendency for the latter to condense. Meteorologists explain in this way the formation of clouds and rain which often follows on a sudden lowering of atmospheric pressure.

When moisture condenses in this way it is peculiarly liable to collect round atoms or particles which are charged with electricity.

The mode of the experiment will now be clear. If there are electron tracks with their electrified débris in a damp gas which is allowed to expand suddenly, the moisture will in the first place condense along the tracks, and these under suitable illumination show as white streaks against a dark background. In this way the paths of the electrons become visible.

In its elements the apparatus is extremely simple (Fig. 110). A cylindrical chamber of a few inches in diameter is formed of metal sides and a glass top. A piston forms the bottom of the chamber: this can be dropped to any desired amount causing the expansion of the air in the

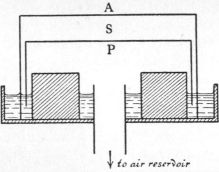

Fig. 110. This drawing shows the main principles of Wilson's expansion apparatus. Within the chamber of which the lid A is made of glass, a piston P can slide up and down. The space below P is connected to a reservoir of air the pressure of which can be varied. It is in the space s that the tracks are observed. It is cut off from the space under P and from the outside air by a water seal as used in a gasometer. If the pressure under P is raised a little, P rides up into the position shown. If then the pressure under P is reduced very suddenly, P comes down with a thud: the air in s expands and is chilled. If there are any tracks of electrons or alpha particles, fog settles on them. They can then be photographed in a bright light.

chamber and the consequent chill. The air is kept moist by the presence of a small quantity of water. The rays which are to be investigated can be shot in through suitable openings in the wall, or may be produced by radioactive substances contained within the chamber.

Examples are given in Plates XXV, XXVI. It will be observed at once that the tracks due to the effect of X-rays begin and end within the chamber. Their broken and irregular form is due to the continual deflections which the electron experiences as it makes its way through the gas. Sometimes the turns are very sharp: in such cases

PLATE XXV

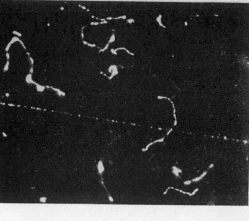

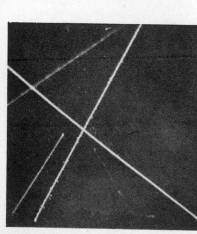

A. The tracks of alpha particles - atoms of helium - which go in a straight line almost from start to finish. The fog drops are so numerous and close that the tracks appear as continuous white lines. These particles are shot away from radioactive substances. (*p. 272*)

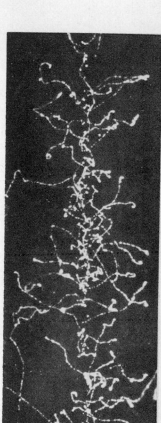

C. This shows a few tracks separately: some of them are due to very fast electrons, beta rays, which move in straight lines in the relatively small portion of their path which is shown in the photograph. The X-rays are proceeding from top to bottom. One of the tracks has so few drops on it that it is barely visible. (*p. 272*)

B. Tracks due to X-rays. The X-rays themselves do not show up at all. They form a fine straight pencil across the middle of the photograph, but no straight lines are to be seen as in XXV C. The visible tracks are of electrons which the X-rays have caused to originate in some of the atoms they have encountered. Their tortuous paths are characteristic: they are too light to maintain already, that the X-rays the alpha rays, because they are bandied about from the atoms they meet. This illustrates the point made already, that the X-rays act through the electron motions which they originate. The X-rays are proceeding from left to right. (*p. 272*)

PLATE XXVI

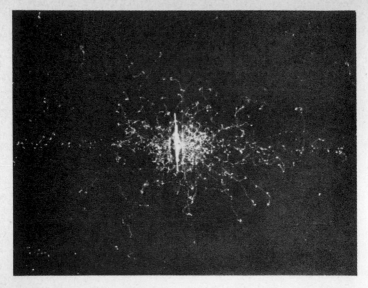

A. In this photograph a fine pencil of rays proceeding from right to left meets a copper screen. It excites a cloud of electrons in the copper; and it will be observed that it has a tendency to carry the electrons with it. There are more on the side where the X-rays emerge after passing through the screen than on the side where they enter. (*p. 272*)

B. A photograph due to the diffraction of electrons (G. P. Thomson.) A stream of electrons has been made to fall upon the surface of a crystal, and the photograph has been placed so as to receive the diffracted beams. (*p. 276*)

the electron has penetrated some way into the atom, having struck it fairly centrally. It has thus come nearer than usual to the nucleus and has swung quickly round it like a comet that has gone near to the sun. The dotted character of the track is due to uneven action on the atoms struck and traversed by the rays. Sometimes a single electron is displaced, sometimes a little group near to one spot: sometimes again an electron is ejected by the primary electron with such violence that by its acquired energy of motion it is able to tear away a few more electrons from atoms which it meets. As the electron nears the end of its path its action becomes more violent. With diminishing speed it stays longer in each atom that it enters, and the results are more serious. In the beginning of its path its higher velocity allows it to traverse the atom quickly and less damage is done. The beta rays shown in Plate XXVc make this much clearer; their speed is so great in some cases that the drops are scattered only thinly along the path, which is then comparatively straight, and the path becomes difficult to distinguish. It will be noticed that the more penetrating the X-rays the longer the tracks of the electrons which they produce.

In a preceding chapter we saw that ultra-violet light was capable of discharging a conductor electrified negatively. This action is identical with that of the X-rays when they set electrons in motion. The ultra-violet light causes an ejection of electrons from atoms on which they fall. The speed in this case is far less, and the effect is only observed under favourable conditions. The electrons move so slowly that the nature of the substance on which the light falls is a matter of importance. Different substances exert small electrical forces of different amounts, hindering the ejection of the electrons. These are far too small to interfere with the actions of X-rays, but in the case of light can obscure the photo-electric effect. Thus a clean zinc surface is easily discharged, while the effect almost ceases when it is allowed to become foul with exposure to the atmosphere.

The longer waves of light have, no doubt, the same power as those that are shorter. They also can act on single electrons within the atoms, but the energy imparted in each case is not enough to help the electron to break away. For this reason it may be that we do not see the rays of the infra-red because the sensitivity of the eye seems to depend on electrical effects, which must consist of electron displacements. So also we may suppose that rays of very short wave-length, ultra-violet, and so forth, are injurious, because the electrons which they set in motion are too swift and have too violent an action. The photographic plate for similar reasons is strongly acted upon by short wave-lengths, and is only with difficulty treated so that it can respond to the infra-red.

The picture thus presented to us of the interaction of electrons and various forms of radiation in its broad outlines is simple and comprehensive. The electron is set in motion in the X-ray tube. It strikes an atom in the target: there and then the energy is transferred to some entity, which has lately received the name of photon. The latter moves in straight lines penetrating various substances to an extent which depends on its energy. Sooner or later these penetrations and traversings of atoms come to an end because one of them is fatal: the photon disappears as such and an electron again carries the energy. The electron as it flies loses energy, an effect from which the photon is exempt, in the process of tearing electrons from the atoms through which it passes. It may at some encounter part with its remaining energy in the act of generating a new photon, and so on. Finally the energy is frittered away in the form of heat or chemical actions. Sometimes, it appears, encounters are not simple: the energy of a photon or electron may be divided between two such entities at one encounter, but these subsidiary phenomena, though intensely interesting and important to the study of the whole matter, cannot be included in this brief description. The main point is that there are two entities, one charged and the other not, both capable of carrying energy through space, delivering it at intervals, each in its own fashion, and capable also of mutual exchange of their burdens.

This conception of light in all its forms is of course at variance, at least in appearance, with the wave theory which has been, and is, so useful. But before attempting any consideration of the contradiction we must go on somewhat further along the same road, where we shall find that there is yet much more to be explained.

Light in its various forms behaves sometimes like a wave and sometimes like a corpuscle: may it not be that entities which we have been accustomed to consider as corpuscular may under some circumstances behave like waves?

The trial has been made, and it turns out that the duality is shown here also. Indeed the effect is very easily demonstrated when the proper arrangements are made: though it has only been in recent years that the realisation of its possible success has led, after much careful searching, to the proper design of the experiment. When a fine pencil of electrons is directed upon a crystal, a diffraction pattern appears, which, though characteristic, is obviously of the same character as a pattern due to X-rays. The example shown in Plate XXVIB is due to G. P. Thomson. The penetration of electrons is extremely small, so that extremely thin crystalline films must be used: alternatively effects may be obtained by reflection from a crystal surface. Once however the technical difficulties are overcome the effect is obvious. Here electrons behave like waves.

Lastly there is the atom itself, which no one has ever thought of as anything else than a particle of matter. The experiment is now more difficult, but it appears likely that in this case also a stream of atoms impinging upon a crystal shows a diffraction pattern. Thus through the whole range of the fundamental entities with which we are acquainted there runs this dual behaviour: all can behave like corpuscles or like waves according to circumstances. Our distinction between radiation and matter becomes one of degree and not of kind.

This short summary of the matter necessarily omits a great number of experimental results, and of theoretical connections and parallelisms which, if they could have been included, would have represented it in bolder lines and greater details. But space and time in their prosaic sense have set a limit.

This widening of our view of the nature of things is surely one of the most remarkable consequences of modern research. No one could have anticipated this fundamental universality. A lifting of the mist has shown us links and similarities in the prospect where we had imagined separations and differences. Light, visible and invisible, X-rays, the emissions of radioactive substances, electrons, matter itself, are now seen to have common properties and to be united in some manner which we do not yet fully understand. The most obvious defect in our appreciation is our difficulty in understanding the nature of that which can at one moment be thought of as a wave, and in the next moment as a corpuscle. How are we to picture this seeming contradiction to ourselves?

Probably we come now to a point where personal leanings lead to a choice in a mode of expression. The facts are that a number of natural phenomena can best be linked together on a wave theory, and another equally striking set can be expressed very clearly in terms of the theory of the corpuscle. Now, as Jeans has already said, we have no right to expect that we should always be able to represent new phenomena and new ideas in terms already in use. Our use of the wave and the corpuscle are each correct in its own place: if we had better illustrations for our use we might better be able to avoid contradiction. Even now, the development of the new subject of wave-mechanics shows how we may gradually feel our way to a better position.

When a local wind raises waves on a limited area of the surface of the sea, the waves travel away as a group, a distinct entity. The velocity of the group as a whole is not that of the waves within it, which continually move through from the rear to the front and there die away. There are two distinct features, the group as a whole, and the waves within it. The group as it goes contains a certain amount of energy: its waves, if their paths cross, will show all the phenomena of interference. Here is a parallelism with the photon in both its characteristic forms. The attempts to express the properties of radiation in this novel way have already been strikingly successful.

It is obvious indeed that we cannot bind for ever any phenomenon and its developments in terms of our present choosing. When Whewell described, in his *History of the Inductive Sciences*, the gradual development of the wave theory of light, he pointed out that every new discovery fitted perfectly into the scheme which the theory prepared for it, and exclaimed that this was the mark of a true theory as against a false: the corpuscular theory of Newton had been set aside, the wave theory had for ever taken its place. This brilliant mind did not foresee the interruption in the latter's continuous success. The two old theories, and no doubt the new wave-mechanics, and conceptions yet unformed, are only of use as ties that bind together groups of discovered phenomena, and enable us to think more clearly and to determine new lines of research. If, as in our present case, there are contradictions which perplex us, they must be due to imperfections in our theories and illustrations: and we need not strain over much to resolve them. The resolution will come in its own time, when research has added to our knowledge and lifted our minds to higher points of view. Meanwhile we have come into possession of a wonderful principle which unites all forms of radiation and all kinds of matter. We may rightly speak of light as constituting the universe when we give the word the full meaning which this prospect reveals to us.

INDEX

A CATALOGUE OF SELECTED
DOVER SCIENCE BOOKS

A CATALOGUE OF SELECTED
DOVER SCIENCE BOOKS

Physics: The Pioneer Science, Lloyd W. Taylor. Very thorough non-mathematical survey of physics in a historical framework which shows development of ideas. Easily followed by laymen; used in dozens of schools and colleges for survey courses. Richly illustrated. Volume 1: Heat, sound, mechanics. Volume 2: Light, electricity. Total of 763 illustrations. Total of cvi + 847pp.

60565-5, 60566-3 Two volumes, Paperbound 5.50

THE RISE OF THE NEW PHYSICS, A. d'Abro. Most thorough explanation in print of central core of mathematical physics, both classical and modern, from Newton to Dirac and Heisenberg. Both history and exposition: philosophy of science, causality, explanations of higher mathematics, analytical mechanics, electromagnetism, thermodynamics, phase rule, special and general relativity, matrices. No higher mathematics needed to follow exposition, though treatment is elementary to intermediate in level. Recommended to serious student who wishes verbal understanding. 97 illustrations. Total of ix + 982pp.

20003-5, 20004-3 Two volumes, Paperbound $5.50

INTRODUCTION TO CHEMICAL PHYSICS, John C. Slater. A work intended to bridge the gap between chemistry and physics. Text divided into three parts: Thermodynamics, Statistical Mechanics, and Kinetic Theory; Gases, Liquids and Solids; and Atoms, Molecules and the Structure of Matter, which form the basis of the approach. Level is advanced undergraduate to graduate, but theoretical physics held to minimum. 40 tables, 118 figures. xiv + 522pp.

62562-1 Paperbound $4.00

BASIC THEORIES OF PHYSICS, Peter C. Bergmann. Critical examination of important topics in classical and modern physics. Exceptionally useful in examining conceptual framework and methodology used in construction of theory. Excellent supplement to any course, textbook. Relatively advanced.
Volume 1. Heat and Quanta. Kinetic hypothesis, physics and statistics, stationary ensembles, thermodynamics, early quantum theories, atomic spectra, probability waves, quantization in wave mechanics, approximation methods, abstract quantum theory. 8 figures. x + 300pp. 60968-5 Paperbound $2.00
Volume 2. Mechanics and Electrodynamics. Classical mechanics, electro- and magnetostatics, electromagnetic induction, field waves, special relativity, waves, etc. 16 figures, viii + 260pp. 60969-3 Paperbound $2.75

FOUNDATIONS OF PHYSICS, Robert Bruce Lindsay and Henry Margenau. Methods and concepts at the heart of physics (space and time, mechanics, probability, statistics, relativity, quantum theory) explained in a text that bridges gap between semi-popular and rigorous introductions. Elementary calculus assumed. "Thorough and yet not over-detailed," *Nature*. 35 figures. xviii + 537 pp.

60377-6 Paperbound $3.50

ALMOST PERIODIC FUNCTIONS, A. S. Besicovitch. Thorough summary of Bohr's theory of almost periodic functions citing new shorter proofs, extending the theory, and describing contributions of Wiener, Weyl, de la Vallée, Poussin, Stepanoff, Bochner and the author. xiii + 180pp. 60018-1 Paperbound $1.75

AN INTRODUCTION TO THE STUDY OF STELLAR STRUCTURE, S. Chandrasekhar. A rigorous examination, using both classical and modern mathematical methods, of the relationship between loss of energy, the mass, and the radius of stars in a steady state. 38 figures. 509pp. 60413-6 Paperbound $3.25

INTRODUCTION TO THE THEORY OF GROUP'S OF FINITE ORDER, Robert D. Carmichael. Progresses in easy steps from sets, groups, permutations, isomorphism through the important types of groups. No higher mathematics is necessary. 783 exercises and problems. xiv + 447pp. 60300-8 Paperbound $3.50

THE SOLUBILITY OF NONELECTROLYTES, Joel H. Hildebrand and Robert L. Scott. Classic, pioneering work discusses in detail ideal and nonideal solutions, intermolecular forces, structure of liquids, athermal mixing, hydrogen bonding, equations describing mixtures of gases, high polymer solutions, surface phenomena, etc. Originally published in the American Chemical Society Monograph series. New authors' preface and new paper (1964). 148 figures, 88 tables. xiv + 488pp. 61125-6 Paperbound $3.00

INTRODUCTION TO APPLIED MATHEMATICS, Francis D. Murnaghan. Introduction to advanced mathematical techniques—vector and matrix analysis, partial differential equations, integral equations, Laplace transform theory, Fourier series, boundary-value problems, etc.—particularly useful to physicists and engineers. 41 figures. ix + 389pp. 61042-X Paperbound $2.25

ELEMENTARY MATHEMATICS FROM AN ADVANCED STANDPOINT: VOLUME I—ARITHMETIC, ALGEBRA, ANALYSIS, Felix Klein. Second-level approach, illuminated by graphical and geometrical interpretation. Covers natural and complex numbers, real equations with real unknowns, equations in the field of complex quantities, logarithmic and exponential functions, goniometric functions, infinitesimal calculus, transcendence of e and π. Concept of function introduced immediately. Translated by E. R. Hedrick and C. A. Noble. 125 figures. ix + 274pp. (USO) 60150-1 Paperbound $2.25

ELEMENTARY MATHEMATICS FROM AN ADVANCED STANDPOINT: VOLUME II—GEOMETRY, Feliex Klein. Using analytical formulas, Klein clarifies the precise formulation of geometric facts in chapters on manifolds, geometric and higher point transformations, foundations. "Nothing comparable," *Mathematics Teacher.* Translated by E. R. Hedrick and C. A. Noble. 141 figures. ix + 214pp. (USO) 60151-X Paperbound $2.25

ENGINEERING MATHEMATICS, Kenneth S. Miller. Most useful mathematical techniques for graduate students in engineering, physics, covering linear differential equations, series, random functions, integrals, Fourier series, Laplace transform, network theory, etc. "Sound and teachable," Science. 89 figures. xii + 417pp. 6 x 8½. 61121-3 Paperbound $3.00

A COURSE IN MATHEMATICAL ANALYSIS, Edouard Goursat. *The entire "Cours d'analyse" for students with one year of calculus, offering an exceptionally wide range of subject matter on analysis and applied mathematics. Available for the first time in English. Definitive treatment.*

VOLUME I: Applications to geometry, expansion in series, definite integrals, derivatives and differentials. Translated by Earle R. Hedrick. 52 figures. viii + 548pp. 60554-X Paperbound $3.00

VOLUME II, PART I: Functions of a complex variable, conformal representations, doubly periodic functions, natural boundaries, etc. Translated by Earle R. Hedrick and Otto Dunkel. 38 figures. x + 259pp. 60555-8 Paperbound $2.25

VOLUME II, PART II: Differential equations, Cauchy-Lipschitz method, non-linear differential equations, simultaneous equations, etc. Translated by Earle R. Hedrick and Otto Dunkel. 1 figure. viii + 300pp. 60556-6 Paperbound $2.50

VOLUME III, PART I: Variation of solutions, partial differential equations of the second order. Poincaré's theorem, periodic solutions, asymptotic series, wave propagation, Dirichlet's problem in space, Newtonian potential, etc. Translated by Howard G. Bergmann. 15 figures. x + 329pp. 61176-0 Paperbound $3.00

VOLUME III, PART II: Integral equations and calculus of variations: Fredholm's equation, Hilbert-Schmidt theorem, symmetric kernels, Euler's equation, transversals, extreme fields, Weierstrass's theory, etc. Translated by Howard G. Bergmann. Note on Conformal Representation by Paul Montel. 13 figures. xi + 389pp. 61177-9 Paperbound $3.00

ELEMENTARY STATISTICS: WITH APPLICATIONS IN MEDICINE AND THE BIOLOGICAL SCIENCES, Frederick E. Croxton. Presentation of all fundamental techniques and methods of elementary statistics assuming average knowledge of mathematics only. Useful to readers in all fields, but many examples drawn from characteristic data in medicine and biological sciences. vii + 376pp. 60506-X Paperbound $2.25

ELEMENTS OF THE THEORY OF FUNCTIONS. A general background text that explores complex numbers, linear functions, sets and sequences, conformal mapping. Detailed proofs. Translated by Frederick Bagemihl. 140pp. 60154-4 Paperbound $1.50

THEORY OF FUNCTIONS, PART I. Provides full demonstrations, rigorously set forth, of the general foundations of the theory: integral theorems, series, the expansion of analytic functions. Translated by Federick Bagemihl. vii + 146pp. 60156-0 Paperbound $1.50

INTRODUCTION TO THE THEORY OF FOURIER'S SERIES AND INTEGRALS, Horatio S. Carslaw. A basic introduction to the theory of infinite series and integrals, with special reference to Fourier's series and integrals. Based on the classic Riemann integral and dealing with only ordinary functions, this is an important class text. 84 examples. xiii + 368pp. 60048-3 Paperbound $3.00

MATHEMATICAL FOUNDATIONS OF STATISTICAL MECHANICS, A. I. Khinchin. Introduction to modern statistical mechanics: phase space, ergodic problems, theory of probability, central limit theorem, ideal monatomic gas, foundation of thermodynamics, dispersion and distribution of sum functions. Provides mathematically rigorous treatment and excellent analytical tools. Translated by George Gamow. viii + 179pp. 60147-1 Paperbound $2.00

INTRODUCTION TO PHYSICAL STATISTICS, Robert B. Lindsay. Elementary probability theory, laws of thermodynamics, classical Maxwell-Boltzmann statistics, classical statistical mechanics, quantum mechanics, other areas of physics that can be studied statistically. Full coverage of methods; basic background theory. ix + 306pp. 61882-X Paperbound $2.75

DIALOGUES CONCERNING TWO NEW SCIENCES, Galileo Galilei. Written near the end of Galileo's life and encompassing 30 years of experiment and thought, these dialogues deal with geometric demonstrations of fracture of solid bodies, cohesion, leverage, speed of light and sound, pendulums, falling bodies, accelerated motion, etc. Translated by Henry Crew and Alfonso de Salvio. Introduction by Antonio Favaro. xxiii + 300pp. 60099-8 Paperbound $2.25

FOUNDATIONS OF SCIENCE: THE PHILOSOPHY OF THEORY AND EXPERIMENT, Norman R. Campbell. Fundamental concepts of science examined on middle level: acceptance of propositions and axioms, presuppositions of scientific thought, scientific law, multiplication of probabilities, nature of experiment, application of mathematics, measurement, numerical laws and theories, error, etc. Stress on physics, but holds for other sciences. "Unreservedly recommended," *Nature* (England). Formerly *Physics: The Elements*. ix + 565pp. 60372-5 Paperbound $4.00

THE PHASE RULE AND ITS APPLICATIONS, Alexander Findlay, A. N. Campbell and N. O. Smith. Findlay's well-known classic, updated (1951). Full standard text and thorough reference, particularly useful for graduate students. Covers chemical phenomena of one, two, three, four and multiple component systems. "Should rank as the standard work in English on the subject," *Nature*. 236 figures. xii + 494pp. 60091-2 Paperbound $3.50

THERMODYNAMICS, Enrico Fermi. A classic of modern science. Clear, organized treatment of systems, first and second laws, entropy, thermodynamic potentials, gaseous reactions, dilute solutions, entropy constant. No math beyond calculus is needed, but readers are assumed to be familiar with fundamentals of thermometry, calorimetry. 22 illustrations. 25 problems. x + 160pp. 60361-X Paperbound $2.00

TREATISE ON THERMODYNAMICS, Max Planck. Classic, still recognized as one of the best introductions to thermodynamics. Based on Planck's original papers, it presents a concise and logical view of the entire field, building physical and chemical laws from basic empirical facts. Planck considers fundamental definitions, first and second principles of thermodynamics, and applications to special states of equilibrium. Numerous worked examples. Translated by Alexander Ogg. 5 figures. xiv + 297pp. 60219-2 Paperbound $2.50

A TREATISE ON THE DIFFERENTIAL GEOMETRY OF CURVES AND SURFACES, Luther P. Eisenhart. Detailed, concrete introductory treatise on differential geometry, developed from author's graduate courses at Princeton University. Thorough explanation of the geometry of curves and surfaces, concentrating on problems most helpful to students. 683 problems, 30 diagrams. xiv + 474pp.

60667-8 Paperbound $2.75

AN ESSAY ON THE FOUNDATIONS OF GEOMETRY, Bertrand Russell. A mathematical and physical analysis of the place of the a priori in geometric knowledge. Includes critical review of 19th-century work in non-Euclidean geometry as well as illuminating insights of one of the great minds of our time. New foreword by Morris Kline. xx + 201pp.

60233-8 Paperbound $2.00

INTRODUCTION TO THE THEORY OF NUMBERS, Leonard E. Dickson. Thorough, comprehensive approach with adequate coverage of classical literature, yet simple enough for beginners. Divisibility, congruences, quadratic residues, binary quadratic forms, primes, least residues, Fermat's theorem, Gauss's lemma, and other important topics. 249 problems, 1 figure. viii + 183pp.

60342-3 Paperbound $2.00

AN ELEMENTARY INTRODUCTION TO THE THEORY OF PROBABILITY, B. V. Gnedenko and A. Ya. Khinchin. Introduction to facts and principles of probability theory. Extremely thorough within its range. Mathematics employed held to elementary level. Excellent, highly accurate layman's introduction. Translated from the fifth Russian edition by Leo Y. Boron. xii + 130pp.

60155-2 Paperbound $1.75

SELECTED PAPERS ON NOISE AND STOCHASTIC PROCESSES, edited by Nelson Wax. Six papers which serve as an introduction to advanced noise theory and fluctuation phenomena, or as a reference tool for electrical engineers whose work involves noise characteristics, Brownian motion, statistical mechanics. Papers are by Chandrasekhar, Doob, Kac, Ming, Ornstein, Rice, and Uhlenbeck. Exact facsimile of the papers as they appeared in scientific journals. 19 figures. v + 337pp. $6\frac{1}{8}$ x $9\frac{1}{4}$.

60262-1 Paperbound $3.00

STATISTICS MANUAL, Edwin L. Crow, Frances A. Davis and Margaret W. Maxfield. Comprehensive, practical collection of classical and modern methods of making statistical inferences, prepared by U. S. Naval Ordnance Test Station. Formulae, explanations, methods of application are given, with stress on use. Basic knowledge of statistics is assumed. 21 tables, 11 charts, 95 illustrations. xvii + 288pp.

60599-X Paperbound $2.00

MATHEMATICAL FOUNDATIONS OF INFORMATION THEORY, A. I. Khinchin. Comprehensive introduction to work of Shannon, McMillan, Feinstein and Khinchin, placing these investigations on a rigorous mathematical basis. Covers entropy concept in probability theory, uniqueness theorem, Shannon's inequality, ergodic sources, the E property, martingale concept, noise, Feinstein's fundamental lemma, Shanon's first and second theorems. Translated by R. A. Silverman and M. D. Friedman. iii + 120pp.

60434-9 Paperbound $1.75

THE PSYCHOLOGY OF INVENTION IN THE MATHEMATICAL FIELD, Jacques Hadamard. Important French mathematician examines psychological origin of ideas, role of the unconscious, importance of visualization, etc. Based on own experiences and reports by Dalton, Pascal, Descartes, Einstein, Poincaré, Helmholtz, etc. xiii + 145pp. 20107-4 Paperbound $1.50

INTRODUCTION TO CHEMICAL PHYSICS, John C. Slater. A work intended to bridge the gap between chemistry and physics. Text divided into three parts: Thermodynamics, Statistical Mechanics, and Kinetic Theory; Gases, Liquids and Solids; and Atoms, Molecules and the Structure of Matter, which form the basis of the approach. Level is advanced undergraduate to graduate, but theoretical physics held to minimum. 40 tables, 118 figures. xiv + 522pp. 62562-1 Paperbound $4.00

POLAR MOLECULES, Pieter Debye. Explains some of the Nobel Laureate's most important theories on dielectrics, including fundamental electrostatic field relations, polarization and molecular structure, measurements of polarity, constitution of simple polar molecules, anomalous dispersion for radio frequencies, electrical saturation effects, connections with quantum theory, energy levels and wave mechanics, rotating molecules. 33 figures. 172pp. 60064-5 Paperbound $2.00

THE CONTINUUM AND OTHER TYPES OF SERIAL ORDER, Edward V. Huntington. Highly respected systematic account of modern theory of the continuum as a type of serial order. Based on the Dedekind-Cantor ordinal theory. Mathematics held to an elementary level. vii + 82pp. 60130-7 Paperbound $1.00

CONTRIBUTIONS TO THE FOUNDING OF THE THEORY OF TRANSFINITE NUMBERS, Georg Cantor. The famous articles of 1895-1897 which founded a new branch of mathematics, translated with 82-page introduction by P. Jourdain. Not only a great classic but still one of the best introductions for the student. ix + 211pp. 60045-9 Paperbound $2.00

ESSAYS ON THE THEORY OF NUMBERS, Richard Dedekind. Two classic essays, on the theory of irrationals, giving an arithmetic and rigorous foundation; and on transfinite numbers and properties of natural numbers. Translated by W. W. Beman. iii + 115pp. 21010-3 Paperbound $1.50

GEOMETRY OF FOUR DIMENSIONS, H. P. Manning. Part verbal, part mathematical development of fourth dimensional geometry. Historical introduction. Detailed treatment is by synthetic method, approaching subject through Euclidean geometry. No knowledge of higher mathematics necessary. 76 figures. ix + 348pp. 60182-X Paperbound $3.00

AN INTRODUCTION TO THE GEOMETRY OF N DIMENSIONS, Duncan M. Y. Sommerville. The only work in English devoted to higher-dimensional geometry. Both metric and projective properties of n-dimensional geometry are covered. Covers fundamental ideas of incidence, parallelism, perpendicularity, angles between linear space, enumerative geometry, analytical geometry, polytopes, analysis situs, hyperspacial figures. 60 diagrams. xvii + 196pp. 60494-2 Paperbound $1.50

FUNDAMENTAL FORMULAS OF PHYSICS, edited by Donald H. Menzel. Most useful reference and study work, ranges from simplest to most highly sophisticated operations. Individual chapters, with full texts explaining formulae, prepared by leading authorities cover basic mathematical formulas, statistics, nomograms, physical constants, classical mechanics, special theory of relativity, general theory of relativity, hydrodynamics and aerodynamics, boundary value problems in mathematical physics, heat and thermodynamics, statistical mechanics, kinetic theory of gases, viscosity, thermal conduction, electromagnetism, electronics, acoustics, geometrical optics, physical optics, electron optics, molecular spectra, atomic spectra, quantum mechanics, nuclear theory, cosmic rays and high energy phenomena, particle accelerators, solid state, magnetism, etc. Special chapters also cover physical chemistry, astrophysics, celestian mechanics, meteorology, and biophysics. Indispensable part of library of every scientist. Total of xli + 787pp.
60595-7, 60596-5 Two volumes, Paperbound $5.00

INTRODUCTION TO EXPERIMENTAL PHYSICS, William B. Fretter. Detailed coverage of techniques and equipment: measurements, vacuum tubes, pulse circuits, rectifiers, oscillators, magnet design, particle counters, nuclear emulsions, cloud chambers, accelerators, spectroscopy, magnetic resonance, x-ray diffraction, low temperature, etc. One of few books to cover laboratory hazards, design of exploratory experiments, measurements. 298 figures. xii + 349pp.
(EUK) 61890-0 Paperbound $2.50

CONCEPTS AND METHODS OF THEORETICAL PHYSICS, Robert Bruce Lindsay. Introduction to methods of theoretical physics, emphasizing development of physical concepts and analysis of methods. Part I proceeds from single particle to collections of particles to statistical method. Part II covers application of field concept to material and non-material media. Numerous exercises and examples. 76 illustrations. x + 515pp.
62354-8 Paperbound $4.00

AN ELEMENTARY TREATISE ON THEORETICAL MECHANICS, Sir James Jeans. Great scientific expositor in remarkably clear presentation of basic classical material: rest, motion, forces acting on particle, statics, motion of particle under variable force, motion of rigid bodies, coordinates, etc. Emphasizes explanation of fundamental physical principles rather than mathematics or applications. Hundreds of problems worked in text. 156 figures. x + 364pp. 61839-0 Paperbound $2.50

THEORETICAL MECHANICS: AN INTRODUCTION TO MATHEMATICAL PHYSICS, Joseph S. Ames and Francis D. Murnaghan. Mathematically rigorous introduction to vector and tensor methods, dynamics, harmonic vibrations, gyroscopic theory, principle of least constraint, Lorentz-Einstein transformation. 159 problems; many fully-worked examples. 39 figures. ix + 462pp. 60461-6 Paperbound $3.00

THE PRINCIPLE OF RELATIVITY, Albert Einstein, Hendrick A. Lorentz, Hermann Minkowski and Hermann Weyl. Eleven original papers on the special and general theory of relativity, all unabridged. Seven papers by Einstein, two by Lorentz, one each by Minkowski and Weyl. "A thrill to read again the original papers by these giants," *School Science and Mathematics.* Translated by W. Perret and G. B. Jeffery. Notes by A. Sommerfeld. 7 diagrams. viii + 216pp.
60081-5 Paperbound $2.00

INTRODUCTION TO SYMBOLIC LOGIC AND ITS APPLICATION, Rudolf Carnap. Clear, comprehensive, rigorous introduction. Analysis of several logical languages. Investigation of applications to physics, mathematics, similar areas. Translated by Wiliam H. Meyer and John Wilkinson. xiv + 214pp.
60453-5 Paperbound $2.25

SYMBOLIC LOGIC, Clarence I. Lewis and Cooper H. Langford. Probably the most cited book in the literature, with much material not otherwise obtainable. Paradoxes, logic of extensions and intensions, converse substitution, matrix system, strict limitations, existence of terms, truth value systems, similar material. vii + 518pp.
60170-6 Paperbound $2.75

VECTOR AND TENSOR ANALYSIS, George E. Hay. Clear introduction; starts with simple definitions, finishes with mastery of oriented Cartesian vectors, Christoffel symbols, solenoidal tensors, and applications. Many worked problems show applications. 66 figures. viii + 193pp.
60109-9 Paperbound $2.00

GUIDE TO THE LITERATURE OF MATHEMATICS AND PHYSICS, INCLUDING RELATED WORKS ON ENGINEERING SCIENCE, Nathan Grier Parke III. This up-to-date guide puts a library catalog at your fingertips. Over 5000 entries in many languages under 120 subject headings, including many recently available Russian works. Citations are as full as possible, and cross-references and suggestions for further investigation are provided. Extensive listing of bibliographical aids. 2nd revised edition. Complete indices. xviii + 436pp.
60447-0 Paperbound $2.75

INTRODUCTION TO ELLIPTIC FUNCTIONS WITH APPLICATIONS, Frank Bowman. Concise, practical introduction, from familiar trigonometric function to Jacobian elliptic functions to applications in electricity and hydrodynamics. Legendre's standard forms for elliptic integrals, conformal representation, etc., fully covered. Requires knowledge of basic principles of differentiation and integration only. 157 problems and examples, 56 figures. 115pp.
60922-7 Paperbound $1.50

THEORY OF FUNCTIONS OF A COMPLEX VARIABLE, A. R. Forsyth. Standard, classic presentation of theory of functions, stressing multiple-valued functions and related topics: theory of multiform and uniform periodic functions, Weierstrass's results with additiontheorem functions. Riemann functions and surfaces, algebraic functions, Schwarz's proof of the existence-theorem, theory of conformal mapping, etc. 125 figures, 1 plate. Total of xxviii + 855pp. 6⅛ x 9¼.
61378-X, 61379-8 Two volumes, Paperbound $5.00

THEORY OF THE INTEGRAL, Stanislaw Saks. Excellent introduction, covering all standard topics: set theory, theory of measure, functions with general properties, and theory of integration emphasizing the Lebesgue integral. Only a minimal background in elementary analysis needed. Translated by L. C. Young. 2nd revised edition. xv + 343pp.
61151-5 Paperbound $3.00

THE THEORY OF FUNCTIONS, Konrad Knopp. Characterized as "an excellent introduction . . . remarkably readable, concise, clear, rigorous" by the Journal of the American Statistical Association college text.

MICROSCOPY FOR CHEMISTS, Harold F. Schaeffer. Thorough text; operation of microscope, optics, photomicrographs, hot stage, polarized light, chemical procedures for organic and inorganic reactions. 32 specific experiments cover specific analyses: industrial, metals, other important subjects. 136 figures. 264pp.
61682-7 Paperbound $2.50

THE ELECTRONIC THEORY OF ACIDS AND BASES, by William F. Luder and Saverio Zuffanti. Full, newly revised (1961) presentation of a still controversial theory. Historical background, atomic orbitals and valence, electrophilic and electrodotic reagents, acidic and basic radicals, titrations, displacement, acid catalysis, etc., are discussed. xi + 165pp.
60201-X Paperbound $2.00

OPTICKS, Sir Isaac Newton. A survey of 18th-century knowledge on all aspects of light as well as a description of Newton's experiments with spectroscopy, colors, lenses, reflection, refraction, theory of waves, etc. in language the layman can follow. Foreword by Albert Einstein. Introduction by Sir Edmund Whittaker. Preface by I. Bernard Cohen. cxxvi + 406pp.
60205-2 Paperbound $3.50

LIGHT: PRINCIPLES AND EXPERIMENTS, George S. Monk. Thorough coverage, for student with background in physics and math, of physical and geometric optics. Also includes 23 experiments on optical systems, instruments, etc. "Probably the best intermediate text on optics in the English language," *Physics Forum.* 275 figures. xi + 489pp.
60341-5 Paperbound $3.50

PIEZOELECTRICITY: AN INTRODUCTION TO THE THEORY AND APPLICATIONS OF ELECTROMECHANICAL PHENOMENA IN CRYSTALS, Walter G. Cady. Revised 1963 edition of most complete, most systematic coverage of field. Fundamental theory of crystal electricity, concepts of piezoelectricity, including comparisons of various current theories; resonators; oscillators; properties, etc., of Rochelle salt; ferroelectric crystals; applications; pyroelectricity, similar topics. "A great work," *Nature.* Many illustrations. Total of xxx + 840pp.
61094-2, 61095-0 Two volumes, Paperbound $6.00

PHYSICAL OPTICS, Robert W. Wood. A classic in the field, this is a valuable source for students of physical optics and excellent background material for a study of electromagnetic theory. Partial contents: nature and rectilinear propagation of light, reflection from plane and curved surfaces, refraction, absorption and dispersion, origin of spectra, interference, diffraction, polarization, Raman effect, optical properties of metals, resonance radiation and fluorescence of atoms, magneto-optics, electro-optics, thermal radiation. 462 diagrams, 17 plates. xvi + 846pp.
61808-0 Paperbound $4.25

MIRRORS, PRISMS AND LENSES: A TEXTBOOK OF GEOMETRICAL OPTICS, James P. C. Southall. Introductory-level account of modern optical instrument theory, covering unusually wide range: lights and shadows, reflection of light and plane mirrors, refraction, astigmatic lenses, compound systems, aperture and field of optical system, the eye, dispersion and achromatism, rays of finite slope, the microscope, much more. Strong emphasis on earlier, elementary portions of field, utilizing simplest mathematics wherever possible. Problems. 329 figures. xxiv + 806pp.
61234-1 Paperbound $3.75

THE THEORY OF SOUND, J. W. S. Rayleigh. Still valuable classic by the great Nobel Laureate. Standard compendium summing up previous research and Rayleigh's original contributions. Covers harmonic vibrations, vibrating systems, vibrations of strings, membranes, plates, curved shells, tubes, solid bodies, refraction of plane waves, general equations. New historical introduction and bibliography by R. B. Lindsay, Brown University. 97 figures. lviii + 984pp.
60292-3, 60293-1 Two volumes, Paperbound $6.00

ELECTROMAGNETIC THEORY: A CRITICAL EXAMINATION OF FUNDAMENTALS, Alfred O'Rahilly. Critical analysis and restructuring of the basic theories and ideas of classical electromagnetics. Analysis is carried out through study of the primary treatises of Maxwell, Lorentz, Einstein, Weyl, etc., which established the theory. Expansive reference to and direct quotation from these treatises. Formerly *Electromagnetics.* Total of xvii + 884pp.
60126-9, 60127-7 Two volumes, Paperbound $4.50

ELEMENTARY CONCEPTS OF TOPOLOGY, Paul Alexandroff. Elegent, intuitive approach to topology, from the basic concepts of set-theoretic topology to the concept of Betti groups. Stresses concepts of complex, cycle and homology. Shows how concepts of topology are useful in math and physics. Introduction by David Hilbert. Translated by Alan E. Farley. 25 figures. iv + 57pp.
60747-X Paperbound $1.25

THE ELEMENTS OF NON-EUCLIDEAN GEOMETRY, Duncan M. Y. Sommerville. Presentation of the development of non-Euclidean geometry in logical order, from a fundamental analysis of the concept of parallelism to such advanced topics as inversion, transformations, pseudosphere, geodesic representation, relation between parataxy and parallelism, etc. Knowledge of only high-school algebra and geometry is presupposed. 126 problems, 129 figures. xvi + 274pp.
60460-8 Paperbound $2.00

NON-EUCLIDEAN GEOMETRY: A CRITICAL AND HISTORICAL STUDY OF ITS DEVELOPMENT, Roberto Bonola. Standard survey, clear, penetrating, discussing many systems not usually represented in general studies. Easily followed by nonspecialist. Translated by H. Carslaw. Bound in are two most important texts: Bolyai's "The Science of Absolute Space" and Lobachevski's "The Theory of Parallels," translated by G. B. Halsted. Introduction by F. Enriques. 181 diagrams. Total of 431pp.
60027-0 Paperbound $2.75

ELEMENTS OF NUMBER THEORY, Ivan M. Vinogradov. By stressing demonstrations and problems, this modern text can be understood by students without advanced math backgrounds. "A very welcome addition," *Bulletin, American Mathematical Society.* Translated by Saul Kravetz. Over 200 fully-worked problems. 100 numerical exercises. viii + 227pp.
60259-1 Paperbound $2.50

THEORY OF SETS, E. Kamke. Lucid introduction to theory of sets, surveying discoveries of Cantor, Russell, Weierstrass, Zermelo, Bernstein, Dedekind, etc. Knowledge of college algebra is sufficient background. "Exceptionally well written," *School Science and Mathematics.* Translated by Frederick Bagemihl. vii + 144pp.
60141-2 Paperbound $1.75

LAPLACE TRANSFORMS AND THEIR APPLICATIONS TO DIFFERENTIAL EQUATIONS, N. W. McLachlan. Introduction to modern operational calculus, applying it to ordinary and partial differential equations. Laplace transform, theorems of operational calculus, solution of equations with constant coefficients, evaluation of integrals, derivation of transforms, of various functions, etc. For physics, engineering students. Formerly *Modern Operational Calculus*. xiv + 218pp.

60192-7 Paperbound $2.50

PARTIAL DIFFERENTIAL EQUATIONS OF MATHEMATICAL PHYSICS, Arthur G. Webster. Introduction to basic method and theory of partial differential equations, with full treatment of their applications to virtually every field. Full, clear chapters on Fourier series, integral and elliptic equations, spherical, cylindrical and ellipsoidal harmonics, Cauchy's method, boundary problems, method of Riemann-Volterra, many other basic topics. Edited by Samuel J. Plimpton. 97 figures. vii + 446pp.

60263-X Paperbound $2.75

PRINCIPLES OF STELLAR DYNAMICS, Subrahmanyan Chandrasekhar. Theory of stellar dynamics as a branch of classical dynamics; stellar encounter in terms of 2-body problem, Liouville's theorem and equations of continuity. Also two additional papers. 50 illustrations. x + 313pp. $5\frac{5}{8}$ x $8\frac{3}{8}$.

60659-7 Paperbound $3.00

CELESTIAL OBJECTS FOR COMMON TELESCOPES, T. W. Webb. The most used book in amateur astronomy: inestimable aid for locating and identifying hundreds of celestial objects. Volume 1 covers operation of telescope, telescope photography, precise information on sun, moon, planets, asteroids, meteor swarms, etc.; Volume 2, stars, constellations, double stars, clusters, variables, nebulae, etc. Nearly 4,000 objects noted. New edition edited, updated by Margaret W. Mayall. 77 illustrations. Total of xxxix + 606pp.

20917-2, 20918-0 Two volumes, Paperbound $5.00

A SHORT HISTORY OF ASTRONOMY, Arthur Berry. Earliest times through the 19th century. Individual chapters on Copernicus, Tycho Brahe, Galileo, Kepler, Newton, etc. Non-technical, but precise, thorough, and as useful to specialist as layman. 104 illustrations, 9 portraits, xxxi + 440 pp.

20210-0 Paperbound $3.00

ORDINARY DIFFERENTIAL EQUATIONS, Edward L. Ince. Explains and analyzes theory of ordinary differential equations in real and complex domains: elementary methods of integration, existence and nature of solutions, continuous transformation groups, linear differential equations, equations of first order, non-linear equations of higher order, oscillation theorems, etc. "Highly recommended," *Electronics Industries*. 18 figures. viii + 558pp.

60349-0 Paperbound $3.50

DICTIONARY OF CONFORMAL REPRESENTATIONS, H. Kober. Laplace's equation in two dimensions for many boundary conditions; scores of geometric forms and transformations for electrical engineers, Joukowski aerofoil for aerodynamists, Schwarz-Christoffel transformations, transcendental functions, etc. Twin diagrams for most transformations. 447 diagrams. xvi + 208pp. $6\frac{1}{8}$ x $9\frac{1}{4}$.

60160-9 Paperbound $2.50

CATALOGUE OF DOVER BOOKS

EINSTEIN'S THEORY OF RELATIVITY, Max Born. Relativity theory analyzed, explained for intelligent layman or student with some physical, mathematical background. Includes Lorentz, Minkowski, and others. Excellent verbal account for teachers. Generally considered the finest non-technical account. vii + 376pp.
60769-0 Paperbound $2.50

PHYSICAL PRINCIPLES OF THE QUANTUM THEORY, Werner Heisenberg. Nobel Laureate discusses quantum theory, uncertainty principle, wave mechanics, work of Dirac, Schroedinger, Compton, Wilson, Einstein, etc. Middle, non-mathematical level for physicist, chemist not specializing in quantum; mathematical appendix for specialists. Translated by C. Eckart and F. Hoyt. 19 figures. viii + 184pp.
60113-7 Paperbound $2.00

PRINCIPLES OF QUANTUM MECHANICS, William V. Houston. For student with working knowledge of elementary mathematical physics; uses Schroedinger's wave mechanics. Evidence for quantum theory, postulates of quantum mechanics, applications in spectroscopy, collision problems, electrons, similar topics. 21 figures. 288pp.
60524-8 Paperbound $3.00

ATOMIC SPECTRA AND ATOMIC STRUCTURE, Gerhard Herzberg. One of the best introductions to atomic spectra and their relationship to structure; especially suited to specialists in other fields who require a comprehensive basic knowledge. Treatment is physical rather than mathematical. 2nd edition. Translated by J. W. T. Spinks. 80 illustrations. xiv + 257pp.
60115-3 Paperbound $2.00

ATOMIC PHYSICS: AN ATOMIC DESCRIPTION OF PHYSICAL PHENOMENA, Gaylord P. Harnwell and William E. Stephens. One of the best introductions to modern quantum ideas. Emphasis on the extension of classical physics into the realms of atomic phenomena and the evolution of quantum concepts. 156 problems. 173 figures and tables. xi + 401pp.
61584-7 Paperbound $2.50

ATOMS, MOLECULES AND QUANTA, Arthur E. Ruark and Harold C. Urey. 1964 edition of work that has been a favorite of students and teachers for 30 years. Origins and major experimental data of quantum theory, development of concepts of atomic and molecular structure prior to new mechanics, laws and basic ideas of quantum mechanics, wave mechanics, matrix mechanics, general theory of quantum dynamics. Very thorough, lucid presentation for advanced students. 230 figures. Total of xxiii + 810pp.
61106-X, 61107-8 Two volumes, Paperbound $6.00

INVESTIGATIONS ON THE THEORY OF THE BROWNIAN MOVEMENT, Albert Einstein. Five papers (1905-1908) investigating the dynamics of Brownian motion and evolving an elementary theory of interest to mathematicians, chemists and physical scientists. Notes by R. Fürth, the editor, discuss the history of study of Brownian movement, elucidate the text and analyze the significance of the papers. Translated by A. D. Cowper. 3 figures. iv + 122pp.
60304-0 Paperbound $1.50

AN INTRODUCTION TO FOURIER METHODS AND THE LAPLACE TRANSFORMATION, Philip Franklin. Introductory study of theory and applications of Fourier series and Laplace transforms, for engineers, physicists, applied mathematicians, physical science teachers and students. Only a previous knowledge of elementary calculus is assumed. Methods are related to physical problems in heat flow, vibrations, eletcrical transmission, electromagnetic radiation, etc. 828 problems with answers. Formerly *Fourier Methods*. x + 289pp. 60452-7 Paperbound $2.50

INFINITE SEQUENCES AND SERIES, Konrad Knopp. Careful presentation of fundamentals of the theory by one of the finest modern expositors of higher mathematics. Covers functions of real and complex variables, arbitrary and null sequences, convergence and divergence. Cauchy's limit theorem, tests for infinite series, power series, numerical and closed evaluation of series. Translated by Frederick Bagemihl. v + 186pp. 60153-6 Paperbound $2.00

INTRODUCTION TO THE DIFFERENTIAL EQUATIONS OF PHYSICS, Ludwig Hopf. No math background beyond elementary calculus is needed to follow this classroom or self-study introduction to ordinary and partial differential equations. Approach is through classical physics. Translated by Walter Nef. 48 figures. v + 154pp. 60120-X Paperbound $1.45

DIFFERENTIAL EQUATIONS FOR ENGINEERS, Philip Franklin. For engineers, physicists, applied mathematicians. Theory and application: solution of ordinary differential equations and partial derivatives, analytic functions. Fourier series, Abel's theorem, Cauchy Riemann differential equations, etc. Over 400 problems deal with electricity, vibratory systems, heat, radio; solutions. Formerly *Differential Equations for Electrical Engineers*. 41 illustrations. vii + 299pp. 60601-5 Paperbound $2.00

THEORY OF FUNCTIONS, PART II. Single- and multiple-valued functions; full presentation of the most characteristic and important types. Proofs fully worked out. Translated by Frederick Bagemihl. x + 150pp. 60157-9 Paperbound $1.50

PROBLEM BOOK IN THE THEORY OF FUNCTIONS, I. More than 300 elementary problems for independent use or for use with "Theory of Functions, I." 85pp. of detailed solutions. Translated by Lipman Bers. viii + 126pp. 60158-7 Paperbound $1.50

PROBLEM BOOK IN THE THEORY OF FUNCTIONS, II. More than 230 problems in the advanced theory. Designed to be used with "Theory of Functions, II" or with any comparable text. Full solutions. Translated by Frederick Bagemihl. 138pp. 60159-5 Paperbound $1.50

INTRODUCTION TO THE THEORY OF EQUATIONS, Florian Cajori. Classic introduction by leading historian of science covers the fundamental theories as reached by Gauss, Abel, Galois and Kronecker. Basics of equation study are followed by symmetric functions of roots, elimination, homographic and Tschirnhausen transformations, resolvents of Lagrange, cyclic equations, Abelian equations, the work of Galois, the algebraic solution of general equations, and much more. Numerous exercises include answers. ix + 239pp. 62184-7 Paperbound $2.75

CATALOGUE OF DOVER BOOKS

INTRODUCTION TO ASTROPHYSICS: THE STARS, Jean Dufay. Best guide to observational astrophysics in English. Bridges the gap between elementary popularizations and advanced technical monographs. Covers stellar photometry, stellar spectra and classification, Hertzsprung-Russell diagrams, Yerkes 2-dimensional classification, temperatures, diameters, masses and densities, evolution of the stars. Translated by Owen Gingerich. 51 figures, 11 tables. xii + 164pp.
(USCO) 60771-2 Paperbound $2.00

INTRODUCTION TO BESSEL FUNCTIONS, Frank Bowman. Full, clear introduction to properties and applications of Bessel functions. Covers Bessel functions of zero order, of any order; definite integrals; asymptotic expansions; Bessel's solution to Kepler's problem; circular membranes; etc. Math above calculus and fundamentals of differential equations developed within text. 636 problems. 28 figures. x + 135pp.
60462-4 Paperbound $1.75

DIFFERENTIAL AND INTEGRAL CALCULUS, Philip Franklin. A full and basic introduction, textbook for a two- or three-semester course, or self-study. Covers parametric functions, force components in polar coordinates, Duhamel's theorem, methods and applications of integration, infinite series, Taylor's series, vectors and surfaces in space, etc. Exercises follow each chapter with full solutions at back of the book. Index. xi + 679pp.
62520-6 Paperbound $4.00

THE EXACT SCIENCES IN ANTIQUITY, O. Neugebauer. Modern overview chiefly of mathematics and astronomy as developed by the Egyptians and Babylonians. Reveals startling advancement of Babylonian mathematics (tables for numerical computations, quadratic equations with two unknowns, implications that Pythagorean theorem was known 1000 years before Pythagoras), and sophisticated astronomy based on competent mathematics. Also covers transmission of this knowledge to Hellenistic world. 14 plates, 52 figures. xvii + 240pp.
22332-9 Paperbound $2.50

THE THIRTEEN BOOKS OF EUCLID'S ELEMENTS, translated with introduction and commentary by Sir Thomas Heath. Unabridged republication of definitive edition based on the text of Heiberg. Translator's notes discuss textual and linguistic matters, mathematical analysis, 2500 years of critical commentary on the Elements. Do not confuse with abridged school editions. Total of xvii + 1414pp.
60088-2, 60089-0, 60090-4 Three volumes, Paperbound $8.50

AN INTRODUCTION TO SYMBOLIC LOGIC, Susanne K. Langer. Well-known introduction, popular among readers with elementary mathematical background. Starts with simple symbols and conventions and teaches Boole-Schroeder and Russell-Whitehead systems. 367pp.
60164-1 Paperbound $2.25

Prices subject to change without notice.

Available at your book dealer or write for free catalogue to Dept. Sci, Dover Publications, Inc., 180 Varick St., N.Y., N.Y. 10014. Dover publishes more than 150 books each year on science, elementary and advanced mathematics, biology, music, art, literary history, social sciences and other areas.